The Fisherman's Guide to North America

by Tom Cofield

GROSSET & DUNLAP
A FILMWAYS COMPANY
Publishers • New York

Art work by Louis Frisino, Dr. Albert Milan and Vernon Grempler.
Photographs in Florida Keys chapter by Bernard "Lefty" Kreh.
World record listing courtesy of Field and Stream Magazine.

Contents

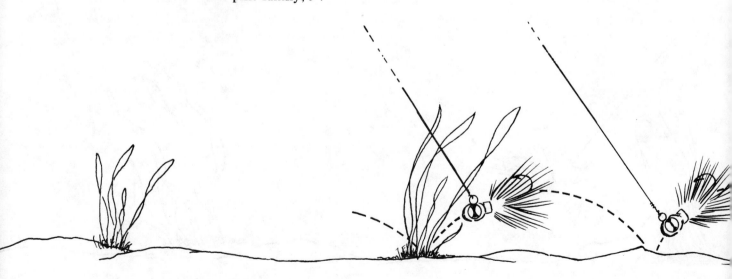

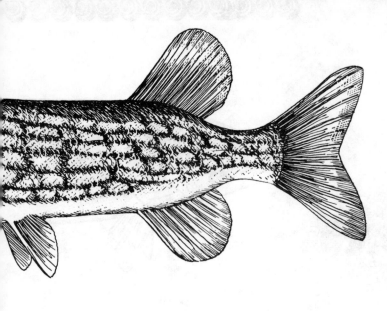

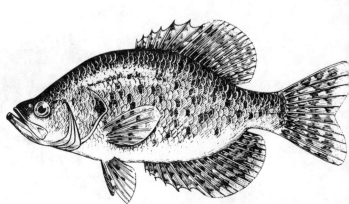

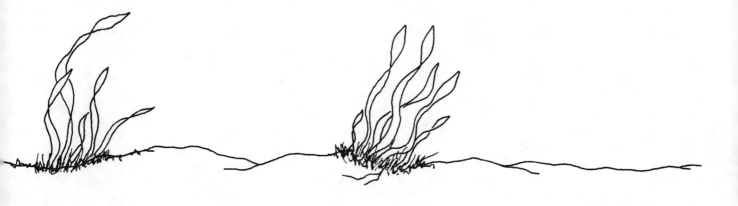

Introduction

Sport fishing is the largest revenue producing, most popular form of recreation enjoyed today by fun-loving, leisure-blessed Americans.

The latest economic survey conducted under the auspices of the U.S. Fish and Wildlife Service revealed that in one year, 1970, sport fishermen in this country spent $5 billion in direct outlay for the privilege of catching fish.

The majority of American anglers, 29,363,000, prefer freshwater fishing over saltwater fishing. Saltwater fans number only 9,460,000.

Of the $5 billion spent in 1970, freshwater fishermen accounted for $3,734,178,000 and saltwater fishermen spent $1,224,705,000.

Allowing that statistical averages often can be misleading and that most economic surveys are regarded more as "indicators" than as finite numbers, there are some valid and valuable conclusions that may safely be drawn from the survey information.

First, freshwater fishermen outnumber saltwater fishermen at least three to one. This in turn may be taken to mean that the majority of American anglers concentrate on those relatively few species of game fish found only in fresh water.

Saltwater anglers show a preference for Atlantic Coast fishing over Gulf or Pacific Coast fishing by a margin of nearly 2½ to one. Here, too, the preference shown is more for species of fish than for geographic location.

In terms of comparative costs, saltwater fishing is more expensive than freshwater fishing. According to the survey, in 1970 freshwater fishermen spent an average of $6.30 per fishing day, while saltwater fishermen spent an average of $10.77 per fishing day.

It should be pointed out that neither figure can be considered accurate in terms of budgeting for fishing trips at today's inflated prices. However, American wage earners are not known to be strict budgeters when it comes to spending money on recreation. Economists studying our frivolous spending habits say we fun-in-the-sun fishing addicts calculate costs by simply "taking along enough money to see us through"; a manifestation of the "credit-card syndrome" now so much a part of the American scene.

Despite the serious cost factor that appears to coexist with sport fishing, this most popular form of recreation is not limited to the more affluent members of our wage-earning society. On the contrary, fishing is a highly regarded and frequently practiced pastime, even among welfare recipients.

To be sure, these unfortunates will not be found in the fighting chairs of offshore fishing cruisers out in the Gulf Stream after marlin. But they can be found lining the railings of highway bridges that span fishable rivers and creeks all over the country.

This does not imply that all bridge fishermen are on welfare. Far from it. There is a whole segment of angling interest directed specifically at bridge and pier fishing. What may be safely concluded, though, is that sport fishing is enjoyed thoroughly by fishermen from one end of the economic spectrum to the other, fancy equipment being no assurance of either success or pleasure.

While freshwater fishermen devoted 592,494,000 days to their sport in 1970, saltwater anglers spent 113,694,000 days trying to catch their favored fish. Unfortunately the survey does not show how many of those fishing days were either total blanks or at best only moderately successful.

For an indication of that most important factor of all, we turn to the results of "creel-census surveys" taken in enough different places, and for both fresh and salt water, to be considered valid information. The conclusion produced by creel-census surveys is that 20 percent of the nation's sport fishermen catch 80 percent of the fish. It is the dedicated purpose of this book to help reverse those percentages.

At the very least we can move through the following pages in a sort of hand-in-hand manner, examining and discussing the basics of sport fishing on a species-by-species basis.

Take heart from the fact that the major difference between a novice fisherman and an expert, or "pro," fisherman is the degree of publicity given the expert's accomplishments—and the total lack of publicity devoted to those blank days we all have but never talk about.

Learning any new skill is a step-by-step progression from one plateau to the next. Therefore, it is my hope that this book will be read, first, from cover to cover, before the fisherman narrows down to the type of fishing and species of fish that he is most interested in.

Many basic techniques of sport fishing apply to numerous species of fish and to both freshwater and saltwater fishing conditions. Still other techniques will be useful only for certain places and conditions or for certain species of fish.

For these reasons a number of sections of this book are devoted to individual species of game fish ardently sought by many Americans. The species included here as "America's Most Popular Game Fish" are those that by virtue of fishing pressure—angler-hours spent on them—have earned a place on that somewhat exalted list.

The list represents a consensus among anglers, both freshwater and saltwater, from all walks of life and from all over the North American continent.

Chapter one

An overview
of U.S. sport fishing

No other nation in the world can match the United States in sport fishing abundance, variety, and distribution.

That is an authenticated fact, not just an expression of American oneupmanship. More important, it means that each beginner is almost certain to find himself or herself surrounded by what amounts to the Gold Medal winners of the world's angling fraternity.

Individualistic almost to a fault in most other aspects, American fishermen have one outstanding trait in common: their abiding eagerness to teach others how to fish and, more to the point, how to enjoy fishing.

Couple the enthusiasm of individual fishermen to the fact that there are at least 50 state agencies and one federal agency dedicated to and charged with the responsibility for increasing sport fishing in this country, and the popularity of this form of recreation becomes more understandable.

Sport-fisheries
management
and how
it grew

In the early days of what now is regarded as modern sport-fisheries management, authorities were badgered by the specter of millions of fishermen fishing for an ever-decreasing population of desirable fish. Added to their woes were projected population growth figures and the corresponding increase in the number of sport fishermen to be satisfied.

Simple arithmetic pointed to one inescapable conclusion. Nature alone could not meet the rising demand for more and more fishing opportunities in more and more widely scattered locations.

Many traditional techniques of fisheries management were put aside in favor of progressive experiments in the transplantation of selected game fish from their native locations to other geographic areas deemed "almost as good." Research programs were launched to find ways of increasing the production of trout hatcheries, then in their infancy. Still other experiments aimed at discovering the results of mixing warm-water species with cold-water species in environments not ideally suited to either one but rated as adequate compromises for both.

Those of us who remember the beginning of this era of fishing miracles are aware that many early experiments bombed badly. And a few mistakes persist in happening even today. Cut-and-try though much of the effort may have been, the overview of sport fishing in this country is one of undeniably outstanding accomplishment.

In addition to all the naturally occurring bodies of water there are now literally thousands of dams impounding countless trillions of gallons of water covering more combined water-acres than existed on the whole North American continent during those supposedly idyllic days when only the American Indian lived here. With rare exception, each lake formed by a dam for water supplies, hydroelectric power, old-fashioned grist mills, or outright recreation complexes is geared to the spread of modern sport fishing.

Advances in trout hatchery techniques have made it possible to supply and maintain fishable populations of brook, brown, and rainbow trout in rivers, streams, and lakes once all but devoid of desirable fish life. The strong flavor of put-and-take fishing in no way detracts from the fact that by those methods fishing opportunities have been provided in abundance in places that otherwise would be barren, as the word is used among fishermen.

Aside from trout hatchery methods, which preceded in terms of success most other experiments, the largemouth bass quickly took center-stage position in fishing-management efforts to transplant and establish fish populations that would, at least partly, sustain themselves in their new homes. Put to the test in a wide variety of "alien" environments, largemouth bass proved to be one of the most adaptable game fish available to fisheries agencies.

Later experiments with smallmouth bass met with only slightly less success. Encouraged, authorities branched out to include, somewhat more selectively, pickerel, northern pike, muskellunge, and, in recent years, coho salmon and white bass.

Some bodies of water into which transplants were released contained native populations of fish in the forage and trash fish categories. Where sufficient forage fish were not present naturally, they were introduced with the game fish to provide a source of food for them until the game fish became, hopefully, self-sustaining.

From a purely scientific standpoint many biologists regarded those early transplantings as dismal failures because, percentagewise, few of them resulted in self-sustaining populations.

Less scientific but more practical heads at administrative levels sought anglers' opinions of the restocking and relocating programs and learned that few anglers were aware of the program, even though they applauded the fishing success they suddenly found. When they were told of the experiments, many fishermen admitted having happily concluded that their own skill had somehow produced the sudden upsurge of fishing success. Fishing authorities were thus able to write an angling truism in their books: fishermen do not look gift fish in the mouth. On the contrary, they are more apt to bask in any sudden fishing success and let those who will question the origin.

Despite advances in the science of oceanography and in knowledge of many oceanic species of game fish, modern sport-fisheries management has been almost totally limited to fresh water and to freshwater species. One obvious reason is the vastness of the nearly unexplorable reaches of the world's oceans.

Beyond regulations controlling legal size and quantities of some fish that may be taken in coastal waters of the United States, little can be done to augment migratory populations, which include the majority of oceanic game fish.

Only striped bass, which are not true ocean dwellers but are classified with saltwater fish, have been transplanted from one coastal region to another—from the Atlantic Coast to the Golden Gate area of the Pacific Coast, with outstanding success. California now has an established and highly cherished population of striped bass zealously guarded against overfishing by legislation restricting quantity of catches and establishing size limits.

Known scientifically as an "anadromous" species (fish that spend most of their lives in salt water but return annually to fresh water to spawn), a sustained striped bass population has been successfully established, admittedly by accident, in the Santee-Cooper Reservoir in South Carolina.

For Atlantic Coast anglers the striped bass ranks among the most popular surf, bay, and river fish available.

Much of the original relocation of largemouth bass took place within states having native bass populations with which to work. From south to north, Virginia, Maryland, Delaware, and New Jersey were among the early progressive states in largemouth bass transplanting.

Maryland, especially, has a wide variety of natural largemouth bass waters ranging from slightly brackish (salt) tidal rivers to totally fresh ponds and lakes. Other than limits on minimum size and daily creels, no restrictions are placed on bass fishing in Maryland.

Maryland also is blessed with one of North America's most unusual rivers: Pocomoke River, an example of untouched natural fishing. Pocomoke River flows through the northernmost stand of cypress and magnolia trees, and is lined on both banks by the nearest thing to a real southern-style cypress swamp one is apt to encounter north of south Georgia or

Louisiana and Florida. Any bass fisherman who has ever dropped a plug or popping bug on the tannic-acid-browned waters of central Florida's cypress swamps would instantly recognize Pocomoke River for what it is—largemouth water. And the bass population is native. There has been no transplanting of bass to or from Pocomoke River.

Maryland's reputation in bass-relocating activities stemmed from programs geared to other regions of the state and to the population of largemouths that has been maintained.

Among outstanding examples of trout-stocking, Shavers Fork of the Cheat River, near Elkins, West Virginia, ranks as the best trout fishing in the eastern United States. Yet, for all practical considerations Shavers Fork is entirely a put-and-take fishery.

Shavers Fork runs through the upper reaches of Shavers Mountain in Monongahela National Forest. Its trout fame would not exist without the state and federal hatchery support it gets—and anyone who thinks that kind of trout fishing is akin to shooting ducks in a rain barrel has a pleasant surprise in store.

Similar praise can be deservedly given to most sport-fishing opportunities in the country that have been more or less created out of whole cloth.

Though not all relocated game fish populations reproduce sufficiently to withstand fishing pressure, catching them can be as dicey in their new homes as it was in their native waters. This is especially true of largemouth bass, smallmouth bass, northern pike, and muskies.

When those same species, plus rainbow trout and striped bass, are mixed in one body of water—as in Smith Mountain Lake, Virginia—most any day's fishing can be fraught with surprises of the kind fishermen dream about.

Smith Mountain Lake was formed when a new standby hydroelectric dam was built. From its birth on the drawing board, the lake was planned as a multiuse impoundment with fishing being secondary only to the needs of the electric power company. Granting the presence of a few largemouth bass in the feeder streams originally, the 50-mile lake with its 500 miles of shoreline would not now be a prime fishing lake had it not been for the efforts and foresight of the Virginia Department of Sportfisheries.

There are thousands of similar examples of the successful creation of sport-fishing opportunities all over the country. A few of us who were privileged to share in some of those early experiments may recall that fishing then was limited to natural populations.

We would react with howls of protest and those dim memories would snap into sharp focus if we were suddenly forced to return to those "limited" times, too often referred to as "the good old days." Some dissenters, happily few in number, lament the fact that we can never return to the days of "all natural fishing." But who wants to?

*What
do we mean
by . . . ?*

In a book such as this one, dedicated to sport fishing and game fish in the United States, it is perhaps fitting that the reader be familiar with those two words as they usually are defined by members of the sport-fishing clan.

Sport fishing may be defined as any attempt to catch fish of any species by hook-and-line for the pure enjoyment to be derived rather than for any expected gain.

Game fish may be defined as those particular species of fish that feed on live prey and that give a good accounting of themselves when hooked by anglers, in terms of the fight they put up for their freedom. Though neither definition should be viewed as a hard-and-fast one, each is accepted by most anglers.

Variations of the game-fish definition abound. For example, if extremely light tackle is used, even a six-inch bluegill could merit the name "game fish."

Coho salmon, recently established in such places as Lake Erie and Lake Michigan, are fun to catch and rank as game fish by all standards other than the relative fight they put up when hooked. There they fall short, compared with other game fish species in the same size range.

The main point, though, is that sport fishing is a form of recreation and, therefore, must be fun. Conversely, if it is fun, then any fish caught, be it game or trash fish, qualifies in the mind of the person doing the fishing. That is all that should be allowed to count in judging either the fish or the fishing.

One of the least valued fish we have in this country is the carp. Carp were introduced here from Germany in the early days of sewage treatment techniques to help rid rivers of raw sewage.

By the time it became obvious that carp were not an answer to the nation's growing sewage problems, those prolific breeders had firmly established their kind and numbers in suitably warm waters all over the country.

Fisheries biologists striving to get more desirable fish established in carp-infested waters say carp not only muddy the spawning waters and kill nests of eggs by smothering them with silt, but they also feed directly on most anything, including unguarded game-fish nests.

Newly filled ponds and lakes thought to be totally devoid of fish life have been "infected" by carp. For a long time nobody knew how it happened. Then biologists discovered that wading birds feeding in the shallows of carp-infested waters waded through carp nests and flew away with some of the eggs clinging to their legs. When the birds landed in other water areas nearby, the eggs would be washed off and would hatch. So by virtue of a step-by-step progression, wading birds helped spread the carp population wherever it could survive— and it survived nearly anywhere it was introduced.

For all their bad qualities—and they are about as undesirable as they can be in the minds of most hook-and-line fishermen—carp can be as "gamy" to catch as any recognized game fish of comparable size. More important, if it were not for the destructive side of the carp population, that species of fish would rank high in terms of spanning a gap that exists for many persons unable for one reason or another to seek the more desirable species.

Although this book deals mainly with the most popular American game fish species, carp are mentioned to focus sharply on one fundamental fact in sport fishing: fishing for any fish that gives pleasure can legitimately be classed as sport fishing, and the devil take opinions to the contrary.

Sport fishermen, sometimes written "sportsfishermen," can be defined simply as fishermen, or fisherwomen, who fish for fun rather than for profit, as contrasted with commercial fishermen.

But the true definition of sport fishermen cannot be so lightly dealt with. As an unofficial fraternity with a membership numbering millions of persons of all ages from all segments of society, the American sport fisherman may be a welfare recipient or a bank president—or even a president of the United States. History shows many were in the clan.

Fishing has been rated as the greatest social leveler ever discovered. During the average working day few men are without hangups of some kind. Some are burdened by prejudice, religious fervor, or outright snobbery. Yet when they meet on a stream, on a riverbank, in a boat, or wherever men gather to fish, it is rare that any notice is taken of a man's skin color, his religion, or even his financial worth.

What will be vigilantly noted is his skill and the number of fish he catches. Thus a bank president or the board chairman of a multibillion-dollar corporation may ask the advice of a bricklayer or a file clerk if either of those two shows more fishing skill than the board chairman or bank president.

The main reason for this freewheeling interchange among social opposites is because fishing skill is no respecter of social or financial status. Neither is it something that can be precisely defined for any man to read about, absorb, and use with assured results. To me, at least, that is one of the most fascinating aspects of sport fishing—it defies precise definition. There are no infallible rules, no fishermen so skilled that they never have a blank day.

If, at first, you don't succeed . . .

The combination of lures, weather, and location that catches fish today may fail to produce a strike tomorrow. And you'll probably never know why. But if you have become addicted to the sport you will keep going back to find out.

On the assurance side of the sport-fishing ledger—those known facts that prevent discouragement—it can be validly assumed that the fish you seek to catch are there to be caught. It remains for you to figure out how.

To accomplish this aim often enough to satisfy your own desire requires that you have a rounded knowledge of the basic principles of sport fishing in general and the specific principles of catching the particular species you are after at any given time. And once you learn these principles, you must practice using them. Without diligent practice, the words in this or any other book on sport fishing would be worthless.

The average sport fisherman has a characteristic willingness to teach others the hows and whys of fishing. His determined effort to hold back information concerning a "new find of fish" or a new method he may have developed for himself is another characteristic.

If you haven't encountered that situation already, be assured you will sooner or later. The dialogue goes something like this: "Hey, Joe, where did you catch those big bass?" Joe can be expected to answer, "Man, that's my secret fishing hole. But I'll take you there next week if you promise not to tell anybody else."

What usually happens is that numerous fishermen have already found the same secret hole, and probably have also taken good friends to share it. Ergo, the secret fishing hole is no secret any more.

The fact that fishermen are willing to take somebody with them to the new find is ample evidence that they are not really being selfish about it. They just want, perhaps unconsciously, to wallow for a time in the distinction of having found something on their own.

Having made at least a nodding acquaintance with *sport fishing, game fish,* and *sport fishermen,* it is now time to get intimately acquainted with the critters all this fuss is about—the fish themselves, species by species, and some of the most widely practiced methods of catching them.

Where should you go for sport fishing? Each of the 50 states offers sport-fishing opportunities. Elsewhere in this book you will find a complete list of state (as well as Canadian province) fisheries agencies, each eager to sell its own state's fishing. Letters to these agencies requesting information on what kinds of sport fishing they offer will bring reams of valuable fishing data for immediate or future use.

Chapter two

Largemouth bass

Any fisherman who gears himself up to meddle with "Old Micropterus" had better be aware that (a) he is joining the ranks of the largest segment of American sport fishing and (b) he most likely will soon become the owner of a tackle box so big that it should rightfully be mounted on wheels with its own source of motive power.

Though professional fisheries biologists may take exception to sweeping statements, the largemouth bass in this country has been rated time after time by popular acclaim as "the number-one game fish" by freshwater anglers.

There are more artificial lures manufactured expressly for catching largemouth bass (and largemouth-bass fishermen) than for any other single freshwater game fish.

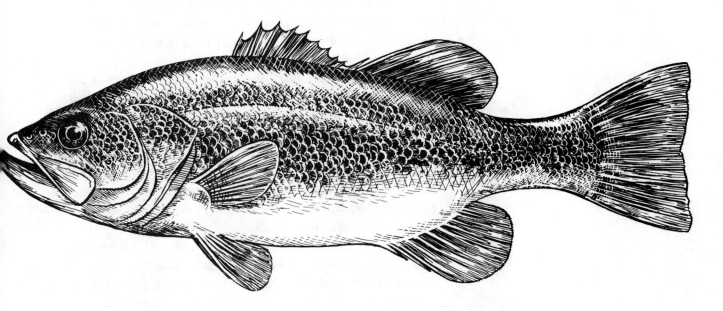

LARGEMOUTH BASS

Micropterus salmoides

World record
22 pounds, 4 ounces

Taken in
Montgomery Lake, Georgia
June 1932

Knowing that perhaps half-a-dozen such lures or plugs would be enough to cover bass-fishing needs throughout the bass's range in no way lessens the urge to buy every new one that pops up on the tackle market. As a result, and almost without exception, the bass fanatics I know all have tackle boxes that resemble hip-roof barns and are darn near as big.

More times than not these collectors of the latest lures use about six of the hundred or more they own and carry on any given bass trip. It would, however, be unthinkable to leave the hip-roof barn at home because who can tell which six lures will be required. That is the rationalization heard most often whenever a colleague suggests lightening the weight in the boat by leaving one tackle box ashore. The answer to such suggestions usually is: "Okay, you leave yours ashore." So both boxes end up in the boat.

Shrewd buyers in most other respects, bass fishermen as a clan are the legal prey of lure manufacturers who crank out variations of old standby plugs, bugs, and spinners nearly every year, dressing them up in new packages and giving them new names, knowing when they do that their flagging sales will soar again. Let one bass fisherman catch a big largemouth on a new or little-known plug and you can be assured that tackle dealers will not be able to keep them in stock for as long as it takes the furor to die.

There is more here, however, than just blatant "suckerism." Since widespread transplanting of largemouth bass in this country took hold, the range of that most popular fish has been extended all over the North American continent, from Canada through the United States into Mexico.

The variety of waters where largemouth bass now are found in fishable abundance ranges from the extreme north to the extreme south; from the bayou country of the south to the cold lake regions of Canada and all in between.

Though most river bass fishing we have is natural, most other types of bass fishing were and perhaps still are the result of put-and-take stocking programs aimed at maintaining populations against fishing pressure. These would include everything from enormous hydroelectric dams and the lakes they have formed down to and including community ponds.

With so much variety of water, bottom conditions, temperature, and available food supply to choose from, who can

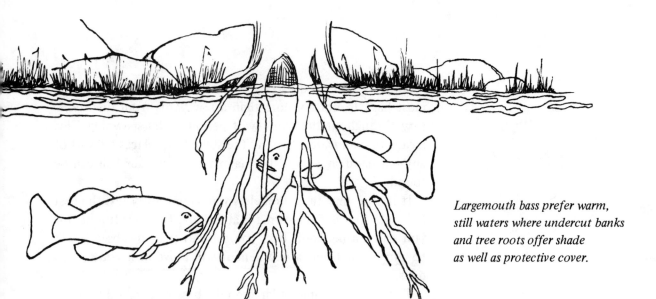

Largemouth bass prefer warm, still waters where undercut banks and tree roots offer shade as well as protective cover.

blame the bass addict for equipping himself to meet any contingency? Anyhow, that's part of the fun.

Aside from variations in feeding habits brought about by different environments in the largemouth's broad range, there are a few characteristics in common regardless of location.

The first of these common denominators, and perhaps the most important to remember, is that largemouth bass do not run in schools, as do many other species of game fish. Adult bass are loners. They will stake out their own territories and will violently defend them against intrusions by other bass.

Except during their spawning periods, which vary with the weather patterns across the continent from late winter to July, each adult bass will take up residence in a place that offers protective cover and a constant supply of live food. Lily-pad beds, sunken logs, tree stumps, undercut banks, underwater ledges and overhangs, or just deep depressions in the lake bed are all sure to be occupied by bass in waters that have an abundant enough population to use up the available hideouts.

In addition, the biggest and most aggressive bass take the best spots; the lesser bass get what's left over. Each spring, after the year's selection has been made and the pecking order is firmly established, those bass without hiding places in the most preferred depths will retreat to deeper water except when they move up to feed.

Because bass are essentially shallow-water fish, most bass hideouts will be found relatively close to shore in water ranging from four feet to about ten feet in depth.

Unless driven to do so by something bigger than they are, most bass do not go more than a few yards from their territory throughout the "lone-wolf period" after spawning. This means that all waters beyond the staked-out places are sort of any-bass-land in which the majority of younger fish can be found.

It is true that these homeless waifs constantly test the best hideouts to see if the owner is still there. It also is true that if you catch a big adult bass you can bet that his absence will be duly noted and a new tenant will move in inside of two days.

The hierarchy among largemouth bass is remarkably parallel to the social distinctions found among humans. There are the "haves" (who inhabit the Nob Hills of a lake, river, or pond) and the "have nots" (who must share their living quarters and food supply until they break out of the "have-not" category by finding a hideout deserted by one of the "haves").

If a smaller bass moves into a bigger bass's hideout after the big fish has been caught, then the smaller bass can stay there only as long as he can successfully defend his position against all comers. And somehow the word gets around among the homeless.

Bass are not finicky

Because they depend upon the availability of live food in any given body of water, bass are not picky eaters. When hungry they will take anything alive that they can get in their mouths and will strike at many creatures they can't even swallow. I have hooked nine-inch largemouths on plugs nearly as big as the fish when they struck and got hung up on the treble-hooks with which most bass plugs are equipped.

Once, while fishing a bass lake near my home, I watched as a swallow dapped the water getting a drink. After dapping almost the same spot three times, the bird swung around and was on the final leg of its fourth dap when about seven pounds of largemouth bass leaped clear of the water and engulfed it in midair.

I have seen a largemouth take a baby duckling that was swimming behind its mother, despite frantic efforts of the mother duck to frighten the bass away. Perhaps she succeeded, in view of the fact that only one duckling met that grim

*Typical largemouth water and
fighting tactics. Note how close
the strike occurred
to the bass's hideout at the base
of the tree.*

25

end. But, knowing bass, I'd be more inclined to think that one duckling was sufficient to satisfy the bass's appetite.

One of the common characteristics among largemouth bass anywhere in their range is their willingness to strike even when not especially hungry.

Though I disagree with those writers who ascribe emotions to a bass's actions, claiming the bass "get mad enough to strike," I believe that plugs and other similar "body-type" lures will evoke strikes from bass if it appears that the unknown creature is trying to invade the territory. Anger, no. The instinct to survive, yes. Man is the only creature known to kill for reasons other than to eat.

To bolster the invasion-of-territory point, many times in many different types of bass water I have found it necessary to cast a bug or plug to the same spot as many as four or five times before getting a strike. Though other bass fishermen may differ, and that is a common trait among us, I interpret such delayed reactions as instinctive caution up to but not beyond the point where the intruder appeared menacing.

However, when bass are in a feeding mood they will take almost instantly whatever lure or plug is cast within their territory, often before the plug hits the water on the first cast. This, along with their willingness to jump when hooked, is part of the reason for the number-one rating of largemouth bass.

Another reason for the top rating is the willingness to take topwater lures. When bass do, they usually burst out with startling violence that has never ceased to be the thrill of all thrills for me.

At least a dozen or more times in my bass fishing life I have had big bass leap clear of the water near my topwater plugs and take the plugs on reentry. Why they did it that way I do not know. But I can assure you I would be a happy man if it happened every day.

I also confess to having lost some of those crazy strikes through sheer excitement upon seeing the fish before it actually struck the lure. It's akin to the "buck fever" most of us have heard about.

To those of us who are addicted to using topwater plugs and bugs for largemouth fishing, the fact that as many or more bass are caught on underwater lures of various types

"Old shoveltail" takes a topwater plug on reentry. Largemouth bass frequently avoid the lure coming out of the water on the initial strike, then take it going back in.

is a cross we have to bear. That addiction also has been the cause of more than a few days of frustration simply because I would not give in and snap on an underwater lure until it was obvious that I had no choice.

Fathers have been known to tell their sons, "Don't do as I do, do as I say." In a similar spirit, I would advise the use of underwater lures, regardless of fishing circumstances or surroundings, until a few bass have been tallied on the personal fishing score.

Underwater lures are a bit easier to use for the beginner since casting accuracy is not nearly as critical as it is with topwater plugs or popping bugs. Where an underwater lure lands is not nearly as important as the path it will travel when you reel it in. In more specific terms, most underwater lures of the "plug" category should be cast beyond the area where you suspect a bass is hiding. Then the lure should be retrieved through or over the selected spot.

Topwater plugs and bugs ideally should be cast right to the spot where you think a bass is lying. If a topwater lure does not evoke a strike within about four feet of where it landed, the chances are it will not produce any with further working toward the boat or bank. Then it's time to pick up for another cast, perhaps to the same spot. Why waste valuable time slowly dragging a lure over unproductive water?

I have seen topwater plugs miss the target by as little as three feet and fail to evoke a strike. When a second, more-accurate cast was made, the fish took the lure. You might say the bass was ready for the plug the second time and would have taken it even if it had landed three feet away. But it has happened enough times and with enough variations in circumstances that I am convinced casting accuracy is primary for topwater fishing.

After the lure hits the water, let it lie still for several seconds before imparting any action. Theoretically, at least, this gives the perhaps startled bass time to eye the disturbing object to determine if it is dangerous. If he decides it is harmless, perhaps he will strike it. Odds are the bass will check out the new object before deciding what to do about it.

Most bass I have taken on topwater plugs or bugs have taken the lures when they were at rest, between "twitches" imparted by the rod tip. Rarely have I taken bass that hit the

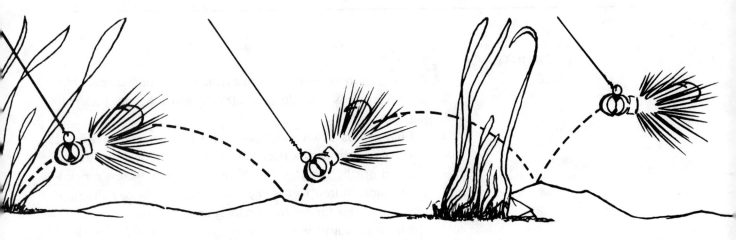

*Bucktails, or jigs,
should be fished
by alternately lifting and dropping
the rod tip while reeling in slowly.
This will cause the jig to bounce
along the bottom.*

lures when they were actually moving or after the lure had been worked more than four feet.

Perhaps because they are "warm-water species," largemouth bass are inclined to be lazier than other fish. Lure motion, for example, is almost always required to catch smallmouth bass, the largemouth's cousins.

Recognizing the best potential bass hangouts in any body of water becomes second nature, an automatic response after only a few successful bass catches.

In general terms, any crop of brush sticking up out of the water offers a legitimate casting target, especially if it seems that the brush is arranged so as to practically assure getting hooked up in it if the cast is bobbled only slightly.

See a spot along the shoreline shaded from the sun by a heavy overhanging growth of vines or tree branches, and if the water is three or more feet deep, you can bet there'll also be a bass there (if your approach hasn't scared it away). If the overhanging brush is so close to the water that it would take a Gold-Medal-winning cast to get a plug in there, then the odds soar for a bass being present.

Mere rhetoric? Don't believe it. Bass pick such places because they afford protection from overhead threats while allowing the bass to lurk in the cool shaded area waiting for minnows and other live food to pass within striking range.

29

LARGEMOUTH TACKLE

Being of more-or-less southern extraction, I confess that given my preferences I would head straight south for my bass fishing trips.

I have at least two good reasons for that preference. First, I know southern bass waters better than those of the midwestern and northern states. In addition, southern waters generally are more suited to the successful use of a fly rod and popping bugs. And for me that really is an addiction.

The largemouth is essentially a southern fish. In its native regions the largemouth will be found in still, warm waters of rivers, small lakes, and ponds usually thick with lily pads and other forms of aquatic growth offering hiding places and shade from the heat of the day.

A true southerner, the largemouth is in tune with the easy living pace normally ascribed to the southern climate.

Because the best southern bass waters rarely become chilled, even in the coolest winter months, all forms of aquatic life there tend to grow and reproduce almost year-round. This in turn means that the bass feed heavily all year and grow accordingly. It also means they can afford to be more selective in their feeding choices. But for reasons best known to the bass themselves, popping bugs accurately presented and properly "worked" seem to send them into a tizzy when little else will.

As you move north and west out of the deep southern states into borderline regions, such as Maryland and Delaware, bass-fishing conditions begin to change from pure south to a mixture of southern, northern, and even midwestern.

With these changes of locale, fishing conditions, and feeding habits, come changes in preferred tackle among bass fishermen. In the overlap regions, spinning tackle is widely used for largemouth fishing. As you move into more northern and midwestern areas, where ponds and rivers give way to big lakes, bait-casting tackle takes over as the tool of preference.

This does not imply that any of the three basic types of fishing tackle (fly rod, spinning rod and reel, and bait-casting rod and reel) cannot be used in any or all types of bass waters.

*Bass galore, but you can leave
a lot of lures hung in the brush.*

It is, however, a matter of the best tools to do the job under the circumstances that exist in each of the three regions.

Assuming that all three types of tackle are available, the type best suited to the potential in a given set of fishing circumstances is the type to use. A wide-ranging bass fisherman will need all three types and should be skilled in the use of each.

For example, the light monofilament spinning line preferred by most spinning fans is not up to the job of horsing a big bass out of the lily-pad beds found so often in the deep south. A bait-casting outfit equipped with braided Nylon or Dacron line testing at least 10 pounds is advised. Oddly, a fly rod and popping bugs are also recommended for such waters because fly leaders can be as much as 10-pound test and because the pressure and leverage exerted by a fly rod are upward, which keeps all but the biggest bass from diving into the depths of weed beds.

An example of a place where all three types of tackle are advisable is Smith Mountain Lake, Virginia.

Smith Mountain Lake, described earlier in this book, is entirely a manmade fishery. It is stocked with largemouth bass, smallmouth bass, rainbow trout, walleyed pike, northern pike, and striped bass (not to mention white bass and coho salmon, which apparently have not taken hold but are there).

The lake is some 50 miles long, beginning near Richmond, and has about 500 miles of shoreline. This means a ratio of inlets, coves, and feeder streams—all prime fishing areas—of ten miles for every one mile of length.

The last time I fished there with guide Paul Beyerle, I got a lesson in the need for all three types of tackle.

Paul had been handling the boat along one of his favorite stretches of fly-rod water, and we had three nice bass in the live-well. When we came to the mouth of a small inlet, he suggested that I put the fly rod down in favor of the bait-casting rod. I had left it ashore. The only thing left for me was a bass action spinning stick equipped with 8-pound monofilament.

As we edged into the mouth of the inlet, Paul suddenly said he saw a big bass and a northern pike lying under an outcropping of brush.

I tossed in a Rapala plug and the bass struck it first, a four-pounder. We fished the entire length of the inlet, about 200

Bass

Largemouth bass, especially the bigger ones, tend to be lone wolves.
Each big bass will stake out and guard its chosen territory against the
invasion of other game fish.

   Even when they are not feeding actively, action can be stimulated by
using large plugs or other types of large lures that seem to threaten the
bass's territory.

Experienced bass fishermen remember each location where they
caught bass, knowing that in a day or two, at the most, another bass
will have moved into the vacant territory. Competition is keen among
bass for the best lurking and feeding areas.

One school of bass expertise holds that most largemouth bass are
caught by being irritated into striking lures that seem to threaten their
occupancy of good territory. This would be a manifestation of the
defensive instinct rather than the feeding instinct.

In many areas where catch-and-release is a popular practice, fin-clipping for later identification and second-catch records adds to our store of bass knowledge.

Of major freshwater game fish, the largemouth bass is the most widely distributed species on the North American Continent. It is rated as the nation's most popular freshwater game fish.

Doc Jacobson "high-rods"
a Smith Mountain Lake largemouth.

yards, and were fishing back out when Paul suggested that now the northern might hit.

When we came within a long cast of the brush pile I dropped that Rapala in the slot again. Having missed that plug once, apparently the big northern was not about to miss it a second time. He struck like an express train, coming out of the water in his first rush.

There I was, with at least 15 pounds of northern pike on a rod and line not up to the job.

His first run nearly stripped all the line off the reel, even though Paul had fired up the outboard and chased him out into the lake.

With his teeth and sharp gill rakers, the outcome was a foregone conclusion. As gently as I played that fish, it just didn't want to be gentled. In less than ten minutes the line parted. The northern swam off with my plug in its jaw.

Stupid? You bet it was. My bait-casting rod was back at the docks equipped with a four-inch length of wire leader on the end of a 15-pound Dacron line. With that outfit I would have landed the pike. It would have been my first for the lake. I didn't take the plug rod because northerns at Smith Mountain Lake were not thought to be active that time of the year. I never again went out on the lake without all three rods.

Be
prepared

There are hundreds of similar manmade lakes in the country with fishing conditions that demand all three types of tackle to insure effective fishing.

An ideal rod-and-reel list for all bass fishing would include: an 8½-foot fly rod equipped with a forward taper "bugging line"; a 5½-foot bait- or plug-casting rod and conventional spool reel equipped with 10- to 15-pound-test braided Dacron or Nylon line; a 7- or 7½-foot spinning rod and open-faced reel equipped with 6- to 8-pound-test monofilament line.

If for economic reasons the number of items on the list must be reduced, an acceptable substitute for the plug-casting rod and reel would be to add an extra spool for the spinning reel. By filling the extra spool with the softest 10-pound-test monofilament, you will bridge at least a part of the equipment gap. The main disadvantage of such a substitution is that it is difficult to cast heavy plugs accurately with the longer, more flexible spinning rod.

34

A good canoe,
a good fishing partner,
and acres of bass water to fish.

LARGEMOUTH FISHING TECHNIQUES

Big-lake bass: Most of the huge, manmade lakes impounded by dams for hydroelectric power, flood control, irrigation, or municipal water supplies offer a full spectrum of "bass cover"—areas in which bass live or maintain feeding stations during peak fishing periods.

Assuming either an established or a put-and-take bass population, big lakes offer challenges to every kind of tackle and technique known to bass fishermen. Popping bugs fished with fly rods; topwater plugs fished with spinning tackle; big, deep-running plugs fished with bait-casting tackle; live-bait fishing with any or all three tackle types—all will be usable to one degree or another, depending upon each lake's physical makeup.

Time of the year and water temperature also have a bearing on what type of tackle and lure to use at any given place.

Though some fishing from shore is possible in many lakes, the most productive bass fishing will be from boats or canoes, usually two men per boat. With two-man teams it is best to have one man use popping bugs or topwater plugs cast toward shore and other likely targets, while the second man casts underwater plugs, spoons, or even spinners parallel to the shore.

Underwater lures should be cast in the direction the boat is drifting to assure presenting the lures before any boat noises spook the fish.

The choice of tackle under those circumstances would be a fly or spinning rod for the topwater work and a stout bait- or plug-casting rod for the heavy underwater lures.

For relatively shallow or middepth regions there are plugs that float when at rest and dive when retrieved.

My own favorite lures in this last category are the Rebel and Rapala plugs, both of which are similar almost to the point of being duplicates. These can be worked to advantage either as topwater or underwater lures. There is no particular choice between those two brand names. The models I prefer for most bass work range in size from about 3½ to 6 inches long. Color preference is the silver scale model.

Floating-diving plugs can be worked to produce surface action or shallow underwater action.

Under all circumstances known to bass fishermen it is safe to say that topwater plugs or popping bugs should be allowed to sit idle for at least a count of five before being "popped" with the rod tip or otherwise worked in any way.

Sinking underwater lures should be allowed time to reach bottom, or near it, before being retrieved. The floating-diving plugs can be used either way, but if depth is desired, an immediate retrieve is needed to get such plugs down where the fish presumably are lying.

The latest innovation in lake fishing for bass is called "structure fishing." The method was developed to its present level of success by tournament bass fishermen using fathometers (depth finders) to locate underwater obstructions, such as ledges, dropoffs, or sunken trees and brush piles, all excellent bass hideouts.

With the upswing in structure fishing has come a number of really deep-diving bass plugs designed to probe waters more than 30 feet deep. Many such big plugs are technically in the floating-diving category. This allows the fisherman to ease line tension if the plug gets hung on an underwater snag, the idea being that it will float free. And, more times than not, that's what happens.

In the live-bait category there are four favored baits: night crawlers (worms), hellgrammites, crayfish (often called "crawdads"), and minnows.

During the hottest months, when water temperatures rise, bass tend to seek cooler depths, abandoning the shallow inshore areas except in the early morning and late afternoon. At such times, drift-fishing frequently pays off in unusual catches of big bass found lurking in the 15- to 30-foot depth zones waiting for the cool of evening before they move inshore.

Drift-fishing is what its name implies. Using either live bait or deep-running plugs, the offerings are made as the boat is allowed to drift with the current or breeze.

Live bait should be cast away from the direction of the drift and should be allowed to settle to the bottom as the boat slowly moves. By "feeling" the baited hook along the bottom it is possible to let it probe into depressions and ledges without getting hung up too often. Deep-running plugs can, of course, be cast in any direction around the drifting boat.

Pond largemouths: Bass ponds are usually about 20 acres or less in area and are fed by springs or small streams. The largest numerical category of bass ponds today are those most accurately described as "farm ponds."

Many farms today have ponds built as sources of water for fire fighting and to water cattle where no other natural supply exists. A secondary benefit accruing to landowners having ponds is a reduction in fire-insurance premiums because of the availability of water.

In addition to farm ponds, many other types of small impoundments have been stocked with fish. These include community ponds and some holding ponds dating back to the days of the old-fashioned water-powered gristmills.

Except in some of the more northern ponds, bass fishing in such relatively small bodies of water is closest akin to fishing the warm, placid, weed-grown waters of southern bayous.

Popping bugs and topwater plugs are most productive, if only because they are less apt to get hung up in lily pads and other growth.

The clear edges of weed beds in ponds are often productive for live-bait fishing, as are deeper reaches of the weedless areas found in the middle of most ponds. Live minnows, especially "shiners," are favored for pond bait fishing. Night crawlers also are good bait, but crayfish and hellgrammites rarely are part of the natural food supply found in warm-water ponds.

River largemouths: Largemouth bass that inhabit rivers usually are wider ranging in terms of feeding territory than are lake or pond bass. This is partly because most rivers have gently sloping bottoms, which in turn means that bass will feed in water depths that are too shallow for hiding places. Observers claim that river bass will forage up and down a length of shoreline shallows looking for minnows and other live food, then retreat to their hiding places to rest.

In rivers affected by tides, many of the best feeding shallows are too shallow for bass during low-tide periods. As a general rule of thumb, then, the best time to fish tidal rivers obviously is at high tide.

There are some notable exceptions to the rule. Rivers bounded by cypress or live oak swamps—which include a lot of prime bass territory in the south—are best fished at low tide when water depth in the brush- and tree-infested areas is too shallow for the fish to maneuver in.

At such times fish will move into the deeper water bordering the swamp edge. During high-tide periods most of the bass will be foraging in the swamp area in spots too far away to reach with a cast, or in places where you would likely never get a hooked fish out of the entangling roots and brush.

Almost without exception in this country, tidal bass rivers are slow moving, insofar as currents are concerned. This means that a slow fishing pace is best. It also means that smaller plugs or popping bugs will be more effective in the shoals normally found in tidal bass rivers. For topwater lures the cast-and-wait method applies in rivers as it does in the still waters of lakes.

Easy does it

Because the best bass waters usually are lush with aquatic grasses, underwater lures should be restricted to the floating-diving type, that can be depth-controlled by the speed of the retrieve, or to spoons having weedless hooks.

Boat docks and piers, moored boats and swimming rafts, high-tide coves and inlets are all part of the scene in most tidal bass rivers. In addition to shorelines, all such objects afford shade, overhead protection, and good feeding stations.

The most effective way to fish a tidal bass river is with foot-by-foot casting toward shore from the maximum distance that will allow accurate casting. Piers and docks should be worked over thoroughly before being passed. Often it is productive to switch from topwater to underwater lures for the deeper waters usually found under and around piers.

*The Texas Floater, as fished
by Dr. J. B. Nail, is a potent
dose of largemouth medicine.*

Doc Nail nails one...

Small but mighty...

The floater is a truck-size
innertube covered in canvas
and fitted with a seat and leg holes
as shown. Movement is slow,
silent, and easy as you

paddle backwards with the feet.
In hot summer months being
half immersed in the water
is a blessing.

LARGEMOUTH BASS LURES

The most popular and productive artificial lures for large-mouth bass include the following categories: *topwater*—fly-rod popping bugs as well as floating plugs; *underwater*—deep-running plugs, spinners, and spoons; *floating-diving*—plugs that are buoyant at rest but dive when retrieved. In this category I include the *plastic worm,* because it is used both as a shallow-running, quick-retrieved lure and as a bottom-fished lure.

Also playing a dual role are those newcomers called *spinner-baits,* which can either be retrieved quickly enough to make them skitter across the surface or slowly enough to let them probe deeper.

In bass fishing, especially, the difference between basic fishing knowledge and the so-called tricks of the trade is the way each angler uses his favorite lures to tally those enviable catches.

In terms of basic knowledge, each category of lure is designed to be fished in a prescribed manner. It is the individual fisherman's variations of those recommended use-methods that can be called the tricks of the trade.

For example, I never met a bass fisherman who could "work" a topwater plug like my father could or who could match him bass-for-bass in total catch or size. Yet, for all of his skill with the "Plunker," or the "Jointed Pikie Minnow" (two of his favorites), he was no great shakes when forced to use underwater plugs of any kind.

As a matter of fact, as built by the manufacturer, the Jointed Pikie Minnow is an underwater plug of the floating-diving variety. As my father used it, however, it was strictly topwater—after he removed the diving scoop on the front and turned the plug upside down. There is no doubt in my mind that he had, over the years, developed his own technique as a result of simply catching fish often enough for the style and pace of his plug work to become a habit.

I know good bass fishermen who are equally uncanny when it comes to "feeling" a deep-running plug over rocky bottoms without getting snagged. This, too, is a developed skill. Still

44

others prefer floating-diving plugs and produce good results by alternating the speed of their retrieves to let the plugs bob up to the surface now and then.

For all of the special touches each bass fisherman may apply, there are certain basic moves that should be made with each different category of lure.

Topwater plugs: The primary purpose of any topwater lure, including fly-rod popping bugs, is to disturb the surface of the water. This is most frequently achieved by short twitches of the rod tip after reeling in all slack.

A rule of thumb followed by most largemouth bass fishermen is to let the plug or bug sit still for about a count of five after it first hits the water. Some wait until the ripples created by the plug or bug have cleared. Then, with a short jerk-and-release motion the lure is "twitched" so it bobs or plops, depending on lure type, the main idea being to move it across the water as little as possible in so doing. This requires a short, sharp flick of the rod tip and is one reason why topwater plug fans prefer short, relatively stiff plug-casting rods.

Some plugs have scooped-out fronts and will, when properly worked, actually bury their noses when twitched and will almost back up on themselves when returning to the surface.

Fly-rod popping bugs are easiest of all topwater lures to twitch with the least motion across the water.

In southern bass waters, or in the summertime in more northern areas, the time between each twitch should be longer than for cooler weather working. Also, the pace of each motion should be varied, such as one pop or twitch, then two, then one again, then three. As noted in previous paragraphs, when a topwater lure has been "worked" without a strike for a distance of about four feet from the spot where it landed, reel it in for another cast.

It is of paramount importance to remember that the longer the cast, the more effort must be put into setting the hook when a bass strikes. Contrary to the belief of some, bass do not always hook themselves, even on plugs having gang-hooks or several sets of treble hooks. Long casts require more effort

Typical popping bugs known to be good for bass fishing

to set the hooks because the longer the line the more stretch there will be. Before you can set the hooks you must first get the line tight.

As one old southern bass fisherman advised: "Man, when you set a hook in one of our bigmouths, hit 'im hard enough to cross his eyes. Then maybe you'll land 'im."

There is, in my opinion, more technique required for successful fishing with a topwater lure than with any other type of bass lure.

Most topwater lures are supposed to represent something crippled trying to get out of the water. The fly-rod popping bugs usually look like large insects while topwater plugs resemble frogs or crippled baitfish. It is that "crippled action" that is vital to effective topwater lure fishing.

All predatory or game fish have at least one characteristic in common. Their prime function in nature's scheme is to rid the waters of weak or crippled bait species.

The underlying reason for this mutually shared function is to assure a continuing strong population of forage species by weeding out all but the best of them. Viewed from another angle, it is selective breeding, in that only the fastest and strongest forage fish are left to breed.

Underwater lures: Underwater plugs, spoons, and spinners are made to represent swimming baitfish or other food.

Each lure type will have an optimum retrieving speed at which it will "swim," or wiggle, best. By reeling each of them in close to the surface where they can be seen, you can determine what reeling speed does the best job of working the plug, spinner, or spoon. The main object is to retrieve underwater lures as slowly as you can and still make them "swim" in a lifelike manner.

Most deep-running plugs are equipped with what I call "diving scoops" on the front. The best of that category will dive deep when retrieved slowly but will float when at rest. Being buoyant to a degree, such floating divers can be "felt" across the bottom, like a baitfish nosing in the mud for food. If the diving scoop catches on a rock or a snag, you can give slack in the line; often the plug will float free of the obstruction. Often this requires only moving the rod in the direction of the line to ease line pressure.

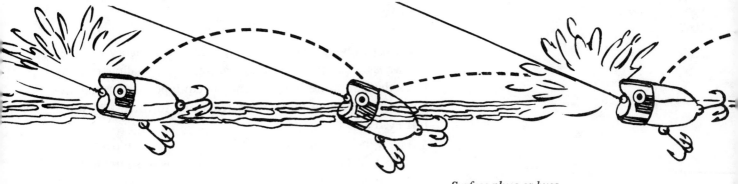

Surface plugs or bugs should be allowed to rest between pops imparted with the rod tip.

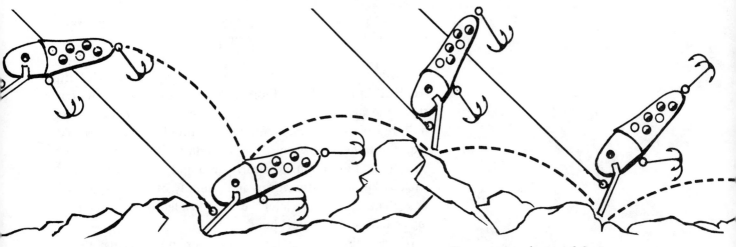

Deep-running plugs work best when retrieved fast enough to bump bottom with each jerk of the rod tip.

Weedless spoons also can be slowly worked over the bottom by lifting the rod tip periodically and imparting a darting action.

Most underwater spinners (not "spinner baits") are made to revolve at one speed. There is little else that can be done to enhance the action other than a twitch of the rod tip now and then. Again, testing the spinner action near the surface where it can be seen will indicate what speed and tip action are best.

Floating-diving plugs: As used here, the category of plugs known as floating-diving plugs means those shallow-running lures that are quite buoyant and are equipped with small diving scoops to take them down from one to three feet when retrieved at a steady pace.

This type of plug can be used effectively in shallow waters, such as will be found most often near brushy shorelines. By letting them float to avoid snags, you can move them out of harm's way on the surface, then reel fast enough to make them dive. It also is possible to use them as surface plugs by using the rod tip to impart a darting action.

Floating-diving plugs of this category are especially good for trolling since they do not probe as deeply as the *deep* runners and are less apt to get snagged. For deeper use, an in-line sinker can be added to the line or leader, preferably between three and four feet from the plug.

Plastic worms: I first ran into plastic worms fishing with Art Hutt in Lake Harris, Florida. An hour or so before we got there a local angler had landed an 11½-pound largemouth bass on a red plastic worm. Art, a reconstituted Yankee, had told me about the red worms, but it hadn't impressed me. But with that 11½ pounder clearly in mind, I bought a small package of red plastic worms and a supply of weedless hooks. Less than three hours later we were headed back to the fishing center with our creel limit.

It was nearly a year later, and after much trying, that I finally caught another bass on those red plastic worms. Casting into the shoreline and retrieving them like shallow-running plugs worked fine in Florida, but no local bass would give the method a nod.

Later, when the plastic worm took over in a sweep across the country, we all learned the various methods of using them and the variety of colors and sizes required for different locales.

Some professional tournament bass fishermen still use plastic worms like floating-diving plugs by casting them right up against the shoreline and retrieving them at a fast pace.

48

*A typical two-day catch
of "keepers" for John Kocher,
including one pickerel.*

In some areas that technique works fine. Certainly it should be tried wherever you go. But the majority of bass taken on plastic worms hit when the worms are fished on or near bottom and at a pace so slow that one wag I know said it is about as exciting as watching grass grow. Fishing the worms on bottom is too slow for my tastes, but I admit it works.

Today's plastic worms come in sizes ranging from about four inches to more than nine inches long, and they come in a variety of colors from purple to sand tan, including red.

Most plastic worm advocates thread the baits on weedless hooks so that the head of the worm lodges behind the eye of the hook. Then they thread a hollow, conical-shaped sinker on the line or leader to add casting weight.

For deep-water fishing the worms are cast out, allowed time to sink to the bottom, then reeled in, about four turns of the reel handle at a time, with a slow upward lift of the rod tip now and then. All in slow motion.

Because they are nearly as lifelike as the real thing, plastic worms usually are taken without suspicion and carried away. By allowing slack in the line as the fish moves off you can give it time to swallow the worm. Then, reel in any excess slack and set the hook, hard.

When cast toward shore and reeled in at a rapid pace, the plastic worm probably resembles a young snake or a fresh-water eel. When fished deep and slow, they probably are taken as worms.

Spinner-baits: Lures classed as "spinner-baits," and hailed as the hottest lures to hit the bass market in a long time, really are not new at all.

I can clearly recall fishing a bayou in south Georgia with a local guide when he showed me how to "dap," as it is called there.

Using a ten-foot bamboo pole, he tied about 36 inches of line to the end and then tied on the first spinner-bait I ever saw. As we neared a chosen fishing spot he showed me how to dap.

Using the bamboo pole to reach out near a cypress bole or a clump of brush, he skittered the big, flopping spinner across the water three or four times before moving on to the next likely spot.

50

Jeff Dane hefts an 8½-pounder
taken from Lochloosa
in north-central Florida
near the town of Orange.

That day he drove me and the bass crazy with that jangling piece of hardware. He drove me crazy because I could not take as many bass as he did. The bass seemed to think it was the best thing since minnows.

What I suppose upset me most was the nonchalant way he lifted bass out of the water as soon as they hit and dumped them unceremoniously in the boat. Some were in the seven- and eight-pound bracket. But with that bamboo pole there was no way to play the fish.

Today, variations of the spinner-bait abound. Many are made by anglers who favor them, but there are numerous models on the tackle market.

They are used most frequently as skittering baits by reeling them in with the rod tip held high enough to keep them up on the surface. They also can be used to probe deep water by allowing them to sink before reeling in.

Live bait: The most popular live baits among largemouth bass fishermen are crayfish, live bull minnows, and live shiners. Night crawlers are at the bottom of the preferred list.

Crayfish, often called "crawdads," are most productive in large lakes during the heat of summer when bass seek cool depths. Hellgrammites, another good bass-catcher, should be hooked through the collar immediately behind their heads and should be fished with as little weight added as possible, and with at least two feet distance between sinker and bait.

Live bull minnows and shiners are hooked in one of two ways: either upward through both lips, or through the dorsal fin. Most minnow fishermen use bobbers, or floats, to tell them when a bass picks up their bait.

By allowing the fish time and slack line to move off with and swallow the bait, you will assure the hook being inside its mouth when you strike.

Enough line should be allowed below the bobber or float to get the baited hook near bottom.

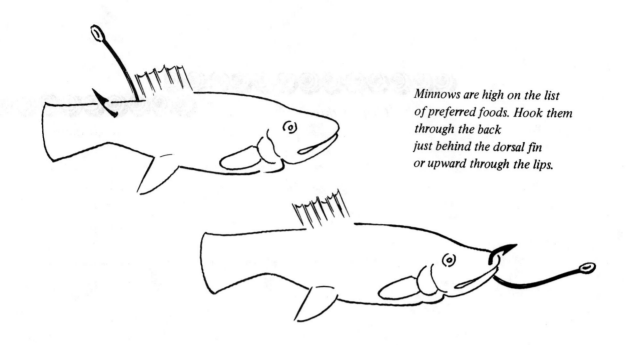

Minnows are high on the list of preferred foods. Hook them through the back just behind the dorsal fin or upward through the lips.

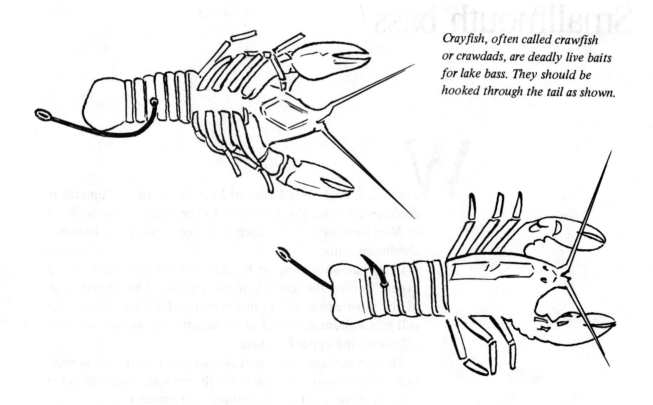

Crayfish, often called crawfish or crawdads, are deadly live baits for lake bass. They should be hooked through the tail as shown.

Chapter three

Smallmouth bass

Without fail, each time I read or hear the word smallmouth it conjures up visions of past trips to the upper Potomac River in Maryland with Lefty Kreh in his old, "Potomac-beaten," aluminum canoe.

Lefty has since gone on to gain national fame as a fishing expert. During the past 15 or more years he has fished some of the most exotic places in the world. Like me, though, he still gets a gleam in his eye at the mention of smallmouth bass fishing on the upper Potomac.

Though nostalgia no doubt plays a part in our mutual reaction, smallmouth bass taken on fly rods and small popping bugs in those swift and sometimes dangerous reaches of the river are the center of our pleasant recollections.

54

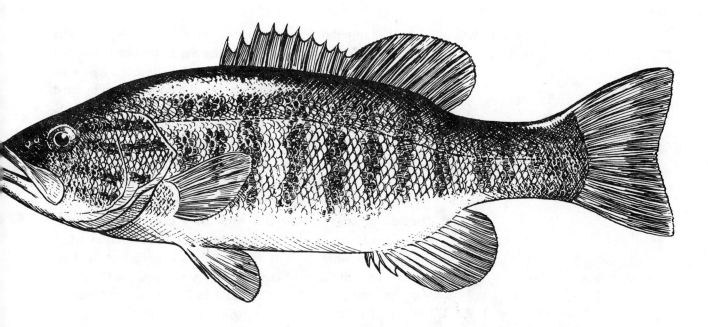

SMALLMOUTH BASS

Micropterus dolomieui

World record
11 pounds, 15 ounces

Taken in
Dale Hollow Lake, Kentucky
July 1955

It is no fisherman's exaggeration when I say that many a day Lefty and I together have hooked a hundred or more smallmouths on a dawn-to-dark float trip down the Potomac. Except for the popping bugs, too big for trout fare, we were rigged for trout fishing. That's the way to take smallmouths on the usually gin-clear Potomac and in most other smallmouth rivers. To me, it is the way to take them anyplace where they can be induced to hit popping bugs.

Having already confessed to being a largemouth bass addict, I as freely admit that smallmouth-bass fishing ranks a close-running second in my book of preferences.

Smallmouth range

Once limited in natural range to the Tennessee River and its tributaries, the Great Lakes and the St. Lawrence River, the upper Mississippi and the Ohio rivers, smallmouth bass now can be found in almost every state in the country and in most of Canada.

Because smallmouths cannot tolerate waters as warm as largemouths like and because they thrive better in cool, swift-running rivers, their total numbers and distribution around the country are limited to areas that can provide those necessities.

In maximum size, smallmouths attain only half the heft expected of largemouths. But what they lack in size is more than made up in sheer knock-down, drag-out action when hooked on suitably light tackle. In fact, none but the long limber rods in the light tackle category will provide the necessary instant give-and-take pressure to land most smallmouths at the height of their leaping fight for freedom.

Most manmade lakes that offer largemouth bass fishing also host good populations of smallmouths. Some of the biggest lakes even have ideal environments for both species. In such places fishermen will find largemouths in the warmer shallows and smallmouths in the cooler depths that they prefer.

Lake smallmouths get bigger than river smallmouths. Some authorities believe it is because river bass have to be more active to fight currents and because their food supply is scarcer.

Similar size differences occur between southern populations and those in the northern and midwestern regions where seasonal weather prevails. Just as southern largemouths grow nearly year-round because there is no real winter weather, so southern smallmouths gain size for the same reasons.

A cool lake,
a congenial companion,
and good smallmouth fishing—
who could ask for more?

For all my happy memories of leaping smallmouths—and they are aerialists of the first order—I cannot agree with those who claim that "pound-for-pound the smallmouth is the fightingest fish we have." To me, such claims are misleading. They tend to spawn disappointment for first-time smallmouth anglers who expect to have their rods snatched out of their hands. Moreover, there is an arm-long list of fish which, pound-for-pound, can make the most active smallmouth look like an advanced case of pernicious anemia.

Though it hasn't happened often, I have caught jack crevalle in the Florida Keys as small as the largest smallmouths I have hooked. After only one such experience, no man would rate the smallmouth in the same league with the jack—or with the bonefish, bluefish, permit, and most of the barracuda I have hooked.

However, recognized for what it really is in the world of game fish, the smallmouth becomes a worthy adversary who will call for every bit of fishing skill that can be mustered.

Generally more wary than the largemouth, smallmouth bass in their native waters are known to strike artificial lures when they are moving more often than when they are at rest. That, in general, is directly opposite to the largemouth's tendency.

This difference is an important point to remember. In the upper Potomac, for example, river currents usually are moderately fast-moving. Smallmouths lurking in their feeding stations must take food quickly as it passes or it will move out of their range. In lakes or rivers having no noticeable current, the tendency seems to persist, though with less consistency.

TACKLE AND TECHNIQUES

Tackle requirements for taking smallmouths are the same as those for taking largemouths: fly rods, spinning rods, and bait- or plug-casting rods. Also, the majority of artificial lures used for largemouths will take smallmouths. Now that relocation and restocking programs are the norm nearly every place where there is a usable body of water, the two related species

Smallmouth bass prefer cooler waters and rocky bottoms. They usually can be found lurking just below ledges of rock or under fallen trees where the water is deep enough close to shore to offer cover.

share most of the manmade sport-fishing facilities in the country today.

Many of the famous bass lakes in northern and north-central Florida host smallmouths as well as largemouths, though the smallmouths do not thrive quite as well as they do in cooler surroundings.

For all practical purposes, fishing techniques for small-mouths (especially in manmade facilities where largemouths are equally present) can be said to be the same as those used for largemouths.

In fact, where both are present, it is not unusual to catch a mixed creel of both on any given day. The only difference I have noted, and it isn't conclusive, is that I have never caught a smallmouth close to where I caught a largemouth. This may be because smallmouths generally seek cooler waters than do largemouths. I have noted that places where small streams enter bass lakes are likely to produce smallmouths, perhaps because of the flow of cooler water.

Variations in lure-handling tactics will produce results in lakes where smallmouths are known to outnumber the large-mouths. In those circumstances it is best to work any lures faster than you would for the smallmouth's larger, slower-moving cousin.

During the hot summer months smallmouths are more likely to retreat to cooler waters and stay there until driven by hunger to move into warmer waters. At such times the best way to fish for them is with live bait: crayfish, hellgrammites, worms, or minnows.

In spring they usually will become active at about 55 degrees Fahrenheit, along with the largemouths. In the fall months northern smallmouths may stay active longer than their southern counterparts.

Natural populations of river smallmouths are a whole new ballgame. Ideally, smallmouth rivers are clear and from cool to downright cold to the human touch. They will have a flow ranging from moderate to swift, with a few long, slower-moving stretches.

The bottoms of good smallmouth rivers usually are rocky and highly productive of aquatic insect life. Take any good trout stream, enlarge it several times, and you have an ideal smallmouth river.

In such rivers smallmouth fishing reaches its peak. The casting rod has no place there, except under rare circumstances in big water. The fly rod and light spinning tackle take over for the most efficiency and the most pleasure.

Fly-rod fans have the broadest scope of lures available to them. Generally, popping bugs should be smaller than the ones you would use for largemouth fishing or for lake small-mouths. In addition, a river smallmouth fisherman can go as far as he likes in the direction of trout-fishing tackle and techniques, including dry flies. I have Wulff pattern Royal Coachman dry flies tied for me (because my eyes have gotten beyond doing it myself) on number 4 hooks. I also have the Irresistible pattern tied the same way. I use both for river smallmouths. River smallmouths will take those two patterns of dry flies even more readily than they take popping bugs.

By using nothing but barbless hooks, I assure myself of a full day of fishing thrills without danger of injuring any of the fish I hook.

In the long, slow-water slicks I switch to spinning gear and small underwater plugs or spinners. There, where the water is deeper and usually not quite as clear, I expect to probe near bottom with whatever lure I use—I also expect to lose a few lures.

For those who prefer spinning tackle for all fishing—and I have no argument against it—the most all-round productive lures are those that fall in the spinner category. In many parts of the country the best known are the Mepps Spinners. There are others as good, and they all come in several sizes, suitable even for ultralight spinning tackle.

Despite the fact that the management tendency today is toward liberalizing bass-fishing regulations, such as eliminating closed seasons, I prefer using barbless hooks, especially for river smallmouths. Barbless hooks enable me to release a fish unharmed, often without even touching it.

I have reservations about fishing for either species of bass during their spawning seasons. But the reader should be aware that those are my personal feelings and that many fisheries authorities do not agree with them. Some experts say that river smallmouths, especially, should be fished heavily and kept to prevent overpopulation and stunted fish.

Such decisions are a matter of personal ethics, for each person to make for himself or herself.

Chapter four

Trout: brook, brown and rainbow

There's something special about trout fishing, even for those trying it for the first time. What's more, the feeling of specialness goes deeper than the usually idyllic surroundings or the sparkling clean water. Nor can it be wholly explained as the effect of a hundred years of written words touting trout fishing as the sport of kings and gentlemen.

Perhaps Izaak Walton came closest to the nub of the matter when he called trout fishing "The contemplative sport," though I'll vow that most of my own troutstream-contemplation has to do with ways and means of catching those wary critters.

Trout fishing probably got its initial boost to an exalted position among anglers a hundred or more years ago, when

BROOK TROUT

Salvelinus fontinalis

World record
14 pounds, 8 ounces

Taken in
Nipigon River, Ontario
July 1916

only gentlemen of means equipped with the finest tackle of that day could catch trout. All others, with their coarse hooks and various "baits," were at extreme disadvantage against men who fished with artificial flies, even as crude as they must have been at that time.

Much of the snobbery of those early days of trout angling remains today—an obsolete and invalid hangover far removed from the 20th-century version of Walton's contemplative sport.

Trout fishing is for anybody

Today, anyone who has the time and means to fish for most other game fish can also fish for trout, assuming the proper equipment and a minimum of instruction. This doesn't mean the sport has slid downhill, though some "purists" say it has. It means that today's scale of living in this country has made it possible for more people to take an active part in what once was reserved for the wealthy.

It also means that the "secrets" of trout fishing and casting with a fly rod have been exposed for what they really are—an easily learned skill, not some God-given special talent.

Where once the landed gentry wouldn't have considered teaching a commoner how to fish for trout, today there are literally thousands of fly-fishing clubs whose main activity is teaching new members how to catch trout and a host of other game fish with fly rods and flies.

To aid and abet this modern reversal of the old snobbish attitude once attached to trout fishing, there now is an arm-long list of trout species and subspecies widely and abundantly distributed in waters throughout the North American continent where prospective trout fans can go to fish with every hope of success.

Granting a difference between a fly-fishing artisan—a purist, a trout expert—and a first-time novice, it is a fact that with a little help in learning how to select "balanced tackle" and how to cast a "straight line," more beginners will catch trout than will fail.

Addictive? You bet!

I recall Steve Cohen and Neil Feldman coming to me for, as they put it, some ideas about where and how to go trout fishing. Both young men were ardent fishermen with years of successful experience behind them in most other types of

Trout

Aside from accurate casting, the next most vital factor in successful trout fishing is the angler's position on or in the stream with respect to the target area being fished.

In general, the angler should be positioned downstream or across-stream from the area to be fished. A study of the accompanying photos will reveal typical stream conditions and ways of fishing them.

Trout always face upstream when feeding. By casting from a downstream position, the angler is assured of not being seen by the trout he is trying to catch in any given pool or riffle.

The across-stream position is used most often when fishing with streamers, spinner-fly combinations, or nymphs.

Even in the best trout streams there is much more barren than productive water. The ability to read stream conditions, to spot the deeper holding pools, the riffles, the rock ledges, the undercut banks—and knowing how to fish each thoroughly before moving on—is a mark of experience.

Comfortable wading boots or wading shoes equipped with nonslip felts are essential.
Wading staffs also are helpful and should be secured to the angler's belt to be easily reached when needed.

sport fishing. But somehow their wide-ranging fishing exploits had never included trout fishing. We made arrangements for a trip to Shavers Fork, West Virginia, mentioned earlier in this book as some of the finest trout fishing in the eastern United States.

As it turned out, the press of deadlines and other workaday distractions allowed for only one fly-casting lesson before we left for Monongahela National Forest, the site of Shavers Fork of the Cheat River, located near Elkins, West Virginia.

With us on the trip (an annual event for us) were Alice and Bill Bristor and Doctor Wayne Jacobson, experts all.

Doc grew up on trout fishing in Wyoming and handles a fly rod as if it were an extension of his arm. He took Steve under his wing and I took Neil in tow. Both rank novices, men who had never cast a fly before in their lives and who had only one casting lesson to lean on, caught trout within the first hour on the stream, and on dry flies.

Granted, Doc and I gave up our own fishing during that hour to make sure the two "greenies" got off to a good start. But they took it from there and caught trout on their own all three days of our stay. What may be even more unbelievable to those who are convinced that fly casting is some kind of magic art, both novices were laying out 50 feet of line and leader like experts.

Sure, a real fly-rod professional, such as Lefty Kreh, could have caught four or five times as many trout and could have laid out close to a hundred feet of line when necessary. The kicker is that Lefty would not have had any more pleasure than those two first-timers did. They now are addicts who call every week with some tale aimed at hastening another trip to Shavers Fork.

To avoid a barrage of brickbats from the nation's trout-fishing pros, let me hasten to say that there are many places and numerous sets of trout-fishing circumstances in which only the pros would take fish, or only the pros would take the biggest fish. But there are more places and more sets of circumstances in which nearly anyone with a modicum of know-how—or the aid of a friendly "tipster"—would also take a satisfactory number of trout.

I suppose the main point at issue here is my personal belief that too many potential trout fans have been turned off by such phrases as "the art of fly fishing" or "trout fishing isn't for everybody," implying that one must be properly anointed before trout will rise to one's fly.

To me that is pure hogwash, generated by understandable pride in and fervor for a sport that deserves an additional dollop of praise over most other kinds of sport fishing. Taken for what it is, and with a shrug of the shoulders, there is no harm in such enthusiasm. In the final analysis, most of the pros I know are ever eager to teach others how to enjoy trout fishing, though I often suspect that the expressed desire to learn from a pro somehow makes such suppliants more acceptable as humans in the eyes of the pros.

How did they get where they are?

Science tells us that all trout are essentially cold-water fish. Original populations are thought to have been Arctic migratory fish driven from the Arctic region by glaciers during the ice ages. When the glaciers began melting and flooded huge land areas, some of the trout population dispersed up streams and rivers all over the world and some remained in the oceans. As the floods receded, the lowering water level trapped trout in those rivers and streams up which they had forged in answer to their migratory instinct. Through evolutionary change those trapped trout populations became the various species and subspecies we know today, each adapting to the environment in which they found themselves stranded.

The Big Three

As important as the numerous subspecies of trout are to scientists, trout-fishing interest in this country today is concentrated on the three best known of them all: brook trout (*Salvelinus fontinalis*), brown trout (*Salmo trutta*) and rainbow trout (*Salmo gairdnerii*).

Of the three, brook and rainbow trout are considered native to this continent. The brown trout originally was a German import. Now all three species are produced and reared in astonishing numbers by federal, state, and commercial trout hatcheries all over the country.

Though a few such hatcheries are devoted exclusively to scientific research on the species, the overwhelming majority of hatcheries are operated solely as sources of supply for restocking rivers, streams, lakes, and ponds on a put-and-take basis expressly for recreational trout fishing.

BROWN TROUT

Salmo trutta

World record
39 pounds, 8 ounces

Taken in
Loch Awe, Scotland
1866

The trout-hatchery expenditures by state and federal agencies are believed to be the largest single economic outlay of its kind in the realm of government-supported recreational activities.

With rare exception, trout fishing in public waters is a government-subsidized sport that seldom even approaches paying its own way through taxes, license fees, or special fishing permits. Many streams having populations of native rainbow or brook trout are restocked either once a year or several times in one year during the peak fishing seasons to offset angler harvests.

*Stocking—
a necessary
"evil"*

At least one segment of the trout-fishing fraternity looks upon put-and-take restocking programs as being in some way fraudulent. Few in number, now, and getting fewer each year, such dissenters lament restocking but apparently refuse to come to grips with the hard fact that without auxiliary restocking there would be little or no "real" trout fishing left today, except in regions so remote as to defy normal angler invasion.

That statement is, unfortunately, true, largely because of the delicate natural balance required to sustain native trout populations at whatever level of abundance is normal for each area.

The encroachment of civilization, even into many wilderness regions formerly considered sacrosanct, inevitably means water pollution in any of its multitudinous forms. Increased deposits of silt, a seemingly harmless inroad against water and bottom purity, can have a marked detrimental effect on natural trout reproduction. Mine acids, now among the most common pollutants, can be lethal in sufficient concentrations; in lesser amounts they can and usually do inhibit the insect food supply. And a decrease in food supply restricts trout growth and reproduction.

Add the annual harvest by millions of trout-fishing fans to the effects of civilization and it is easy to see why few if any native trout populations could sustain themselves.

Once hatchery trout become acclimated to their new surroundings in the stocked streams and lakes, the difference in fighting and eating qualities between them and native trout cannot be measured.

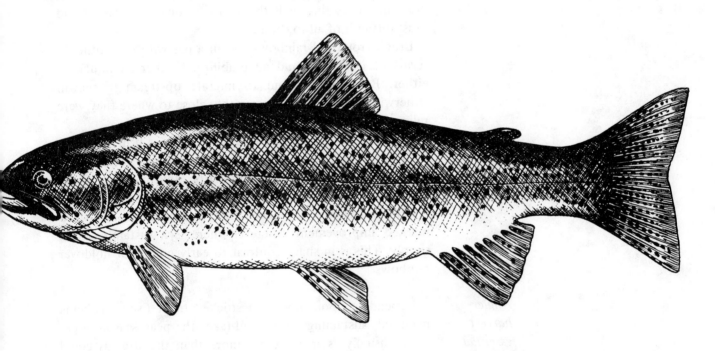

RAINBOW TROUT

Salmo gairdnerii

World record
42 pounds, 2 ounces

Taken in
Bell Island, Alaska
June 1970

In general terms, the three aforementioned species of trout—brook, brown and rainbow—are considered most amenable to hatchery reproduction and rearing.

Brown trout can tolerate warmer waters than either brook trout or rainbows. Brown trout also are considered the hardiest of the three in terms of thriving in surroundings and under circumstances that might be lethal to either brooks or rainbows. Release browns into a slow-moving stream having deep pools and relatively high average water temperatures and in most instances they will thrive, to become the wariest and most difficult of all to catch.

Brook trout and rainbows are on a par with each other in terms of durability and adaptability. Neither has much of either. Brook trout tend to migrate upstream to spawn. Otherwise they will stay reasonably close to where they were released.

Rainbow trout tend to run downstream, as if in answer to their primal urge to migrate back to the oceans of their origin. Over the years of hatchery production, that purely rainbow trait seems to have decreased.

Holdover counts of stocked trout in streams studied show marked improvement wherever there is a sustaining food supply. This is in sharp contrast to early counts of holdover rainbows.

Angler harvest essential

Depending upon how each stocked trout fishery is being managed—sustaining or put-and-take—the peak season population usually is many times more than the streams could maintain over an extended period, say, a year or more.

This means that angler harvest is a tool, a vital requirement of modern management techniques. A companion truism decrees that efficient trout-hatchery production must be maintained at maximum designed output, otherwise the cost-per-trout skyrockets. Similarly it would be a waste of trout-stocking funds, public money, to underfish put-and-take areas and leave a lot of trout to die off over the winter.

What it all amounts to, from a trout fisherman's viewpoint, is an unbelievable number of trout available for restocking purposes all over the North American continent each year. For the most part, each year's production must be dispersed to make room for the next batch.

Releasing trout in warm-water community ponds and small lakes is an outgrowth of the need to produce trout at a planned maximum rate and dispense them each year. Far from being a waste of good trout, the proliferation of community fishing ponds and small recreational lakes has provided excellent sport and similarly excellent table fare for thousands of fishermen who otherwise might never have seen or tasted a trout, or who might never be able to cast a fly over a trout stream.

I know at least a few trout fans who, though they'd choke before admitting it, derive most of their pleasure from properly laying out 60 or more feet of fly line and leader and lightly dropping a dry fly smack in the middle of some chosen trout target area. Whether or not a trout rises instantly to so impressive a cast is secondary to the perfection of the cast itself. Often such persons grade a day's action by how many rises their casts produced instead of how many fish they actually were able to land.

Different things to different people

On the opposite end of the trout scene are those experts, semiskilled beginners, and rank novices who fish for trout with worms for bait where it is legal to do so. The worm fisherman's pleasure in his kind of trout fishing is no less valid than that of the dry-fly purist who wouldn't be caught dead with a can of worms on a trout stream.

In most segments of the fly-angling fraternity, "worm-dunkers" are known as meat fishermen—which gives a deep insight into the fly fisherman's prime motivation: fly fishing, first; fly fishing *catches,* second.

There is much to be said in favor of the fly fisherman's love of fly casting. It is one of the most graceful activities I know when done skillfully.

The smooth, almost liquid flow of a fly line as it snakes out across the water in what seems like slow motion is a sight that never fails to thrill me. When you can couple the esthetics to a few bragging-size trout, then the day becomes part of a cherished bank account of memories that never fade.

Having confessed earlier in these pages to being a confirmed largemouth-bass-fishing addict may not seem to square with my obvious love of trout fishing. If there is an understandable explanation, it perhaps is due to a belief that trout fishing has a deeper meaning than does the rollicking fight between a fisherman and a big largemouth. It is the delicacy and finesse in trout fishing, the appreciation of unblemished wilderness, that keep me going back after trout despite the fact that I rarely keep one.

Though there may be some who will disagree, I believe that many things are more important to the trout-fishing "mystique" than the actual act of fishing. The philosophy of trout fishing; the things about wild scenery that please most people; the quiet that is really not quiet at all but usually a gurgling murmur of sound that can be heard long before the stream is seen; the sudden appearance of deer, black bears, even moose, raccoons, and normally timid rabbits—all of these things combine to make trout fishing what it is: something a little bit different for, yet common to, each individual.

By any standards and through any eyes, trout fishing is what each angler wants it to be. And *this* semiaddicted trout fan is no less affected today after thousands of stream-hours than he was on that first day so many years ago.

TROUT-FISHING TACKLE

The fly rod, fly line and fly reel combined are the tools of the trout-fishing trade. As is true with most other sets of tools, balance is the most vital point to consider.

Though this book will not attempt to teach fly casting, the initial choice of rod, reel, and line is important enough to warrant an explanation of the word "balance," as used in fly fishing.

A fly rod, line, and reel can be said to be balanced when the weight of the fly line is sufficient to flex the rod when casting so that casting energy is produced within the rod itself.

Unlike spin casting or casting plugs with a plug- or bait-casting rod in which the weight of the lure pulls the line off the reel, in fly casting it is the weight of the line that carries the leader and fly to the target.

As the fly rod flexes on the back cast, it stores energy to send the line straight out behind the angler. Then, when he makes his forward cast, the rod again flexes from the weight

of the line. The energy is transmitted from the rod to the line and leader that, in turn, carry the almost weightless fly through the air.

A line too heavy for the rod being used will overload the rod's flexing and energy-storing capacity. The cast will literally run out of energy in midair. This is known as "bogging down" the rod.

Conversely, a line that is too light for the rod being used will not have weight enough to flex the rod so that it will store enough energy to cast the line.

Fly reels are the least important items in the balance of a fly-casting outfit. They serve only to store the line. As long as they are not so heavy that they make the rod-line-reel combination feel butt-heavy, most any fly reel will be satisfactory. Rarely are trout played from the fly reel. Instead, the angler plays the trout by controlling the line with his left hand, assuming a right-handed angler.

Trout prefer moving water and are especially fond of oxygen-charged waters immediately below small waterfalls.

Most fly rods manufactured today are labeled for the proper line weight, based on a numbering system. In addition, most tackle dealers are qualified to advise the customer on this important point.

In addition to proper weight to balance the fly rod chosen, the next most important point to consider in buying a fly line is which of the three types of line will serve you best.

Some lines on lines

The three basic types of fly lines are: level, double-tapered, and weight-forward. Level lines are those having the same diameter throughout. They are the least expensive of the three types and are all that will be required for live-bait fishing.

Double-tapered fly lines are larger in diameter in the middle and taper gradually down to each end. The practical effect of this is to give the angler two lines in one, since he can reverse the line on the reel if one end is worn or if the finish on the line is damaged so that it will no longer float.

Double-tapered lines are most favored by fly casters and are considered essential for trout fishing.

Weight-forward lines are those made with the larger diameter closer to one end than to the other. This provides casting weight to flex the rod and to help carry wind-resistant lures, such as large flies or bugs.

Weight-forward lines are used mostly by bass fishermen or saltwater fly fishermen in conjunction with popping bugs and heavy streamer flies.

For trout fishing, the floating double-tapered line is the one to buy. I specify a "floating line" because there are lines made to sink for other types of fishing. To a trout fisherman they would be useless.

Being relatively expensive, fly lines should be air-dried and cleaned after each day's fishing. Use only the prepared cleaner that comes with each line.

Modern fly lines are coated with plastic to resist water absorption. But after prolonged use, especially where pollen or dust is present, the collection of such "dirt" on the line will cause it to sink. Hence the term "cleaning" the line is more accurate than "dressing" the line. Line dressing was used years ago when fly lines were made of silk intricately woven but lacking in waterproof qualities other than those applied with various dressing materials then in vogue.

It is not the purpose of this book to teach fly casting. That subject has been adequately covered by books specifically written for the purpose. In my opinion several lessons from a fly-casting friend, along with study of written works on the subject, will quickly put the reader on a trout stream with sufficient casting ability to catch trout. As in most other endeavors, practice will bring perfection in fly casting.

What I do hope to impart in this book are the basics of fly fishing for trout. I know from years of experience in teaching others how to catch trout that the most skilled fly caster could come away from a stream empty handed if he didn't know the hows, whys, and whens of fly fishing. By the same token, I have seen first-time fly casters who barely could lay out a straight 30 feet of line catch trout 12-to-the-dozen when instructed about which fly to use and where to cast it.

As noted earlier, there will be times and circumstances when even the experts find it difficult to take trout. Obviously, under those conditions a novice would be even less likely to succeed. Fortunately, those really tough days are the exceptions that prove the rule and are part of trout fishing.

There are several hundred different patterns of flies used to take trout. Each pattern was either developed through angler experimentation and selected as a pattern based on success or passed down from the days of Izaak Walton's exploits with a few modern variations thrown in.

Despite their total numbers, all artificial flies are tied to represent various stages of aquatic insect life, minnows, or terrestrial insect life usually found near streams where they naturally become part of the food chain.

Even the famed Royal Coachman pattern, said to represent no insect known to man, appears as insect life to the trout that take them so avidly throughout most of the North American continent.

By popular definition, the word "fly" may be taken to mean any artificial lure made essentially of fur, feathers, wool, and occasionally tinsel or other shiny materials. Flies

FLY-FISHING TACTICS

are tied for many species of game fish other than trout. But those tied for trout are tied on exceptionally fine-wire hooks to match the delicacy of the fly itself.

All trout flies fall into one of four categories: dry fly, wet fly, nymph, and streamer fly. In general terms, dry flies are made to float. Wet flies are tied with water-absorbing materials so that they sink readily. Nymphs and streamers also are underwater lures. Each category has its own prescribed use-methods.

Dry flies: Because dry flies are made to represent insect life that has just hatched in the stream, they must float to be most effective.

To assure the floating quality, even with new flies, they should be treated with dry-fly dressing, available at any fresh-water-oriented tackle shop. More important, dry flies should be redressed after each fish caught on them or the mouth slime from the fish will cause them to sink.

If that statement appears to be out of chronological order, you're right. It is noted at this point because failing to dress dry flies is the most common initial error made by novice trout fishermen.

I recall Bill Bristor's first session with dry flies. Bill has done at least as much trout fishing as I have, but his favorite method was using streamers and wet flies. He always claimed he couldn't cast well enough to handle dry flies.

After a casting lesson or two I urged him to try dries. Later, after having watched his initial efforts, I checked back with him and found him sitting on the bank with a disgusted look on his face. When I asked him why, he opened his fly box and showed me a dozen or more soggy and hard-used flies. He had not dressed them before using them, and after each fish he caught he changed flies until he had gone through his whole supply. He really thought that was it for the day.

It was my fault for not making sure he knew about the need for dressing and how to use it. So we cleaned up his flies, dressed them, and he was back in business. The event taught us both a lesson. I learned never to take anything for granted when dealing with a novice dry-fly fisherman. Bill learned how many trout can be taken on one dry fly before it must be discarded.

Typical dry fly patterns

General trout-fishing tactics begin with the fact that trout always face the current, or upstream, when feeding. They do so because that way they can see food as it comes to them and have a chance to determine if it is something they want or not.

This, in turn, means that whatever pool, gravel bed, or slick there is should be fished from the down-current end first, working up-current with each successive cast until the pool has been thoroughly fished.

Dry-fly fishing is an upstream method. In other words, the flies are cast upstream so that they float naturally with the current, just as an insect would that had just hatched.

If you cast to the upstream end of a pool or gravel bed first, the line will lie on the water in front of trout that have not seen the fly. Most times that is enough to spook them; they will refuse to take anything until they settle down.

Though there are conditions in which a dry-fly fisherman cannot wade the stream itself and therefore must walk along the shoreline, the overwhelming majority of trout streams are shallow enough to be wadable. Good trout water also is clear enough to easily see the stream bottom to determine water depths. Properly equipped with hipboots or chest-high waders, an angler can pick his way along most streams as quickly as is needed for thorough coverage of the stream.

Upon entering a stream, the dry-fly fisherman should fish the downstream spots first, as noted above, then begin lengthening his casts to reach progressively upstream as far as he can cast accurately. When he has fished a "reach," he may then move upstream for another segment.

One good way for a novice to learn dry-fly fishing is to share a stream with an experienced friend. Each man should take one side of the stream. Using the middle of the stream as a guide, each fishing his own side from the middle to the shoreline, the novice will get a show-and-tell lesson in how it is done. One such lesson usually is enough to let the student go off on his own.

Wet flies: As their name implies, wet flies are tied of materials that will enable them to absorb water and sink readily. Just as there is dry-fly dressing to make dries float, so there is wet-fly dressing to assist the wets in absorbing water on the initial casts. Some wet-fly material gets wet somewhat reluctantly, and it is best to dress them the first time they are used on any given day. Wet flies and streamers may also be dressed to sink more readily by moistening them with saliva.

Wet-fly-fishing techniques begin with the fact that wet flies usually are tied to represent aquatic or stream-bottom insect life that has just hatched and is rising to the surface to spread its wings in flight.

Natural insect life in that stage of development drifts underwater with the current until it sheds the last remains of larval shell. Some species of insects rise to the surface quickly and are usually represented by dry flies, while others drift for longer periods underwater and are taken there by feeding trout in regions where the insects have not yet surfaced.

As is true in fishing most flies, both wets and dries, the essential point of fishing technique is to make the lure "free-float" with the current as a natural insect would.

This means that care should be taken to avoid letting the line or leader tighten enough to move the fly any way other than the way it would move on a natural drift. Trout can instantly spot a fraud by the way it drifts with the current and will usually refuse offerings that do not appear natural.

To accomplish the aim of natural appearance, it is best to cast up and across the current, fishing from one side of the stream or pool at a time.

Again, it is best to fish the areas nearest your position first. For example, if you are fishing from one side of the stream,

Wet flies are made to resemble natural underwater life.

your first casts should be to the middle reaches rather than all the way across. This will permit presentation of the fly to trout in the middle before you cast your line across them to reach the far side. Wet flies may be drifted almost to a total downstream position as long as the line and leader do not drag the fly unnaturally. Then the fly should be cast up and across again for another drift.

A wet fly should always be cast far enough up current from the pool, gravel bed, or any other target to assure it sinking deep before it reaches the area suspected of harboring trout.

By following the drift of the line and the fly with the rod tip, you will get a maximum float or drift for each cast. Though good trout occasionally take wet flies so gently that you may not notice the strike, the majority of wet fly strikes are felt instantly; you can set the hook with a slight but quick lift of the rod tip.

A good thing to remember in all trout fishing is that trout hooks are made of fine wire and are needle sharp. It takes very little effort or tip movement to sink the hook deep enough to land the fish, even with the barbless hooks now favored by many confirmed trout fishermen, including this one.

Nymph fishing: Nymphs are the larval stages of aquatic insects, one step before the wet-fly stage. Of all fly-fishing techniques used to catch trout, nymph fishing is rated the most difficult to do successfully. Yet, for those who master the method, properly fished nymphs will take trout when nothing else will.

I know a number of trout fishermen whose annual score exceeds mine by several times, and who are as inept with dry flies as I am with nymphs.

Doc Jacobson, for example, can "comb" trout out of places with nymphs where I have failed with dries, wets, and streamers. He admits resorting to nymphs only when dry flies fail to produce because, like me, he prefers the surface action one gets with dry flies.

Basically, nymphs are fished like wet flies except deeper. To be most effective, artificial nymphs must bounce and roll along the bottom, and they are tied heavily enough to accomplish that aim.

Nymphs are taken close to the bottom, and strikes frequently are missed because the trout take them gently and usually move with the current for a short distance after taking the fly. It is that "short distance" that causes most losses because anglers do not realize that they have had a strike (or a pickup, as it is called).

As gently as nymphs usually are taken, however, a small pause or slight jerk in the fly line as it drifts usually signals a pickup. Then you strike to set the hook. Many times the line jerk is caused by the nymph getting momentarily hung on a rock, and you will strike nothing. But experienced nymph fishermen strike each pause, regardless of their hooking average.

The big problem with nymph fishing is the fact that as quickly as "nymphing trout" pick up such flies, they even more quickly spit them out as frauds. The trick to learn is how and when to sink the hook before it is expelled. And that takes a heap of practice, which cannot be taught by mere words printed on any page.

Nymph fishing is a skill that should be learned by any angler who wants to get the most out of each trout trip, for assuredly there will be times and conditions that will require nymphs to avoid a blank score.

Various nymphs, supposed
to resemble the larval stages
of certain insects

Streamer flies: Streamers, or streamer flies, are tied on longshanked hooks, usually to represent live minnows. There are borderline streamer patterns that serve both as true streamers or as large wet flies, depending upon how they are used.

Streamer fishing is the least complex of all trout fly-fishing techniques. It differs from wet-fly fishing in that a tighter line is employed along with some fly action imparted by twitches of the rod tip.

The cast should be up and across the stream, as with wet flies, and the line should be taken in to assure minimum slack as the streamer "swims" downstream. Once the streamer reaches an absolute downstream position, it can then be worked through a pool or near protruding rocks and other trout hideouts on a tight line until the cast has been thoroughly fished out. Then cast again for a different drift until the area within easy casting distance of the angler has been thoroughly fished.

Streamers may also be used by letting them "swim" erratically up and down for short distances while adding slack to let them finally drift into a likely hole or under a promising rock ledge or undercut bank, downstream.

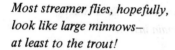

Most streamer flies, hopefully, look like large minnows—at least to the trout!

Because streamers are fished on a relatively tight line, most strikes are felt instantly. It also is true, at least theoretically, that trout strike streamers more vigorously than they strike flies that represent insects.

Spinning tackle: I have a brother-in-law who would willingly declare open war on anyone caught fishing a trout stream with spinning tackle (and he is not alone in his conviction). But no discussion of modern trout fishing would be complete without recognizing that fully a third of today's most avid trout fans use spinning tackle with frequencies ranging from seldom to all the time. What is more important, they do so successfully and with a perfect right to fish the way that pleases them most, assuming no local laws ban the use of such equipment.

Personal preferences aside, there are water and stream conditions that dictate the use of spinning tackle in place of fly rods. Though good trout streams seldom are muddied by normal rainfall, being mostly rocky- or gravel-bottomed and bordered by well-brushed banks, heavy rains often raise the water level and make it murky, if not downright muddy.

Under high, murky water conditions ordinary dry flies, wet flies, and nymphs are virtually useless. At such times the spinner/streamer, or spinner/wet-fly combinations are best because the small spinners normally used in conjunction with flies for trout serve as attractors that glitter even in murky water.

In addition, some deep pools harbor big trout that seem to prefer larger offerings, especially when there is no natural hatch of insects to stimulate feeding. At such times a spinner/fly will entice strikes when other lures will not.

The main reason for using spinning tackle with spinner/fly combinations instead of fly tackle is because spinner/flies are heavy enough to be miserable to cast with a fly rod and just about the right weight to be cast with ultralight spinning tackle. Some are light enough to require a small piece of split-shot for accuracy or to get the spinner-fly down deep enough against a rapid current, such as might occur in a rain-swollen stream.

Another equally valid reason for using spinning tackle for trout centers around those persons who either do not like fly

82

casting or cannot seem to master it to their own satisfaction. Spinner/fly combinations also are effective in trout ponds and lakes, or in rivers where heavy water is the norm.

Though spin fishermen rarely use dry flies, they can and do use wet flies, streamers, and nymphs with telling effect when enough split-shot is added to the lines to afford adequate casting weight. In the case of many ultralight spinning sticks, that doesn't take much to accomplish.

For at least five years before she learned to cast dry flies, Alice Bristor used an ultralight spinning outfit on Shavers Fork.

Her favorite lure was and still is a spinner/fly combination called "The Dabney Special," consisting of a 0/0 spinner ahead of a wet fly, originated by Dabney Kisner.

Alice's score for Shavers Fork would make many a man blush with shame. She has caught more trout in the 18-inch-and-over size bracket than any man I know, including her husband, Bill. Even now, after she learned to adequately cast

Using a special float to add casting weight, flies and streamers can be fished with light spinning tackle.

83

dry flies with her fly rod, she will revert to her spinning rod and reel at the first lull in dry-fly action. And, more times than not, she will take fish.

Though Bill may not appreciate the fact, in that husband-wife trout-fishing team Alice has consistently topped Bill's record for size if not quantity.

Purists just have to face the fact that there are times and circumstances in which a spinning rod will outfish a fly rod, regardless of who is using the fly rod.

The green inchworms that drop from trees during certain times of the year are easily duplicated by tying green wool or other yarns on trout hooks. Though that particular fly is used on fly rods, it is even more efficient when a piece of split-shot is added to the line to get it down deeper and quicker. With the split-shot added, the casting weight is such that it would be better cast with spinning tackle.

After tackle, what? Assuming the acquisition of basic fishing tackle, the most important equipment for trout-fishing comfort and effectiveness is firm, comfortable footwear that will increase your sure-footedness when wading.

Regardless of personal choice or ability to afford hipboots, chest-high waders, or an old pair of khakies and sneakers, all footwear used for wading trout streams should be equipped with "felts."

As the name implies, felts are made of thick, closely woven felt. Nothing I have found gives so much stability of footing on the normally slippery rocks to be found in most trout streams.

Felts may be bought in kit form with a supply of the cement needed to glue them on ordinary sneakers, hipboots, or chest-highs. If price is not a problem, both boots and chest-highs can be bought already equipped with felts.

The difference in wading comfort and peace of mind with and without felts has to be experienced to be fully appreciated. In a word, with felts you can concentrate on fishing instead of on how to keep from a dousing when moving along the stream bed.

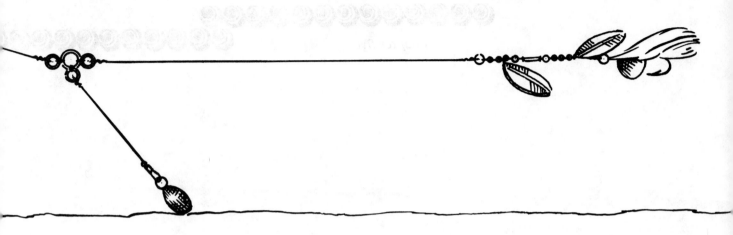

Streamer trolling rig for trout
in lakes and ponds

Chapter five

Shad: white and hickory

No treatise on American sport fishing would be complete without a chapter on both white shad and hickory shad.

Known as "the poor man's salmon" among anglers who have fished for the species during annual spawning runs, the American, or white, shad is the larger of these two members of the herring family.

The hickory shad is equally if not more active when hooked than its larger cousin. It should be added, however, that neither lacks a violent response to being hooked on light tackle.

Atlantic Coast populations of shad are most abundant from North Carolina northward to Connecticut, but their total Atlantic coastal range extends from the St. Lawrence River to the St. Johns River in Florida.

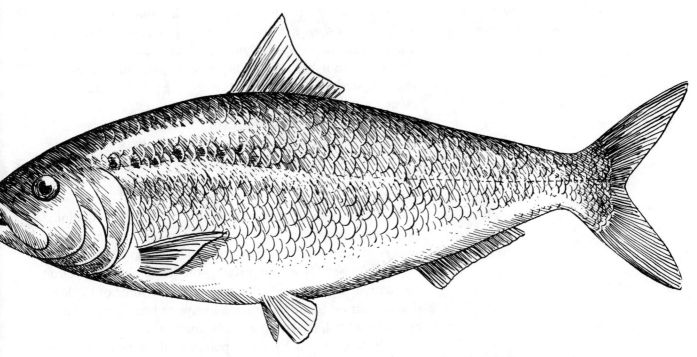

WHITE SHAD

Alosa sapidissima

World record
9 pounds, 2 ounces

Taken in
Enfield, Connecticut
April 1973

Although shad were successfully introduced about 1871 into Pacific Coast waters and now range from southern California to Alaska, sport fishermen in the Pacific range have not had quite the degree of hook-and-line sport enjoyed by their Atlantic Coast cohorts. In the Pacific range the shad is regarded more as a commercial fish, albeit not one of high value.

*Population
decrease . . .*

Unfortunately, it must be reported that since 1900 the annual catch of shad has decreased to about one-third of what it once was. Biologists studying the decrease in shad population attribute it both to the building of dams that block the shad's upstream migration to its spawning grounds and to the shocking increase of water pollution.

Shad are among those species of fish called "anadromous," meaning they live in the ocean most of their lives but migrate to fresh water to spawn, then return to the ocean along with their young of the year.

*. . . and
possible
remedies*

Despite an estimated two-thirds loss of overall population, the annual spawning run of shad up rivers known among anglers for this seasonal sport still produces significant sportfishing catches. More important, the remaining one-third population is considered adequate to restore some of the loss if ways can be found to provide upstream passage over dams by means of fish ladders and similar methods.

In rivers damaged by water pollution there appears to be little if any hope that shad migrations can be restored. Shad instinctively return to the rivers of their origin, just as do salmon and other anadromous fish. Once they are driven out of spawning waters by pollution or other factors, few shad ever return.

The battle against water pollution boils down to a matter of value judgments in the realm of economic priorities. Halting industrial and municipal destruction of water quality by passing and enforcing stringent antipollution laws aimed at restoring once-prolific fish-spawning habitats may mean severe economic setbacks. Of course, the alternative is to close your eyes to pollution and let the environment suffer.

In the meantime, and for however long it continues, shad fishing is like catnip to the nation's felines.

Conowingo Dam in Maryland, one of the top shad fishing areas on the east coast.

Each spring, about the time the dogwoods begin to bloom, hickory shad can be found swimming up the rivers of their range in huge schools. They will continue their upstream surge into small creeks wherever there is enough unpolluted water in which to carry out their active spawning rites.

The white shad characteristically are deeper-water fish that seemingly prefer to stay in the main rivers where suitable gravel beds or rocky bottoms exist to furnish their spawning needs. There are exceptions to that preference, usually when a smaller stream has heavier than ordinary flow, which provides deeper water narrowly confined between banks.

Both species of shad are plankton feeders. They have no oral equipment to take larger food, such as minnows.

From examination of shad stomachs, it is believed that shad feed not at all or rarely during the spawning period. Yet, despite this, shad readily strike the numerous variations of small shad lures used universally throughout the shad's range.

Some authorities believe that shad strike shad lures because of some form of parental concern, that those lures represent a threat to the eggs as they are being spawned and fertilized. Few if any anglers care to debate this point, especially while the shad run is on each spring.

Fishing techniques

Limited to light tackle by the almost weightless lures, most shad fishing is done with fly or spinning rods and reels. When taken on such wands, both hickory and white shad jump like miniature tarpon as well as using the currents to gain their freedom—which they do with ego-disturbing frequency.

The hickory shad may reach a weight of about four pounds. The average weight of white shad is about six pounds, although they have been known to reach eight pounds. In either league, that is a lot of leaping, gyrating fish to land in relatively swift water on light tackle.

Recommended fishing techniques for taking hickory shad in small streams do not vary much from one end of the shad's range to the other. Anglers usually cast their shad lures up and across the current, either from shore or wading with hip-boots, allowing lures to sink as close to bottom as possible while swinging in an arc downstream. The lures usually are reeled in a few turns at a time, along with flicks of the rod tip to provide additional lure action.

The same up-and-across-current technique is used for taking white shad from the banks of suitable rivers.

Where the water is clear enough, schools of shad will be plainly evident. When not on an in-progress spawning run, the fish tend to idle in the current facing upstream. Then, as though on some signal, they will become agitated. An entire school will begin to pair off and move upstream into the nearest riffle or gravel-bed area. Such times and events will

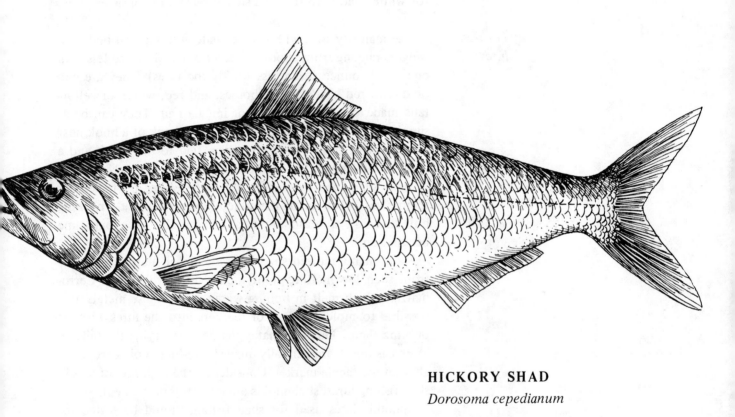

HICKORY SHAD

Dorosoma cepedianum

No world record established

provide peak fishing activity. At other times, when the fish are just waiting for the signal, catches are sporadic.

There appears to be no set pattern or time-of-day preference among either hickories or whites for their spawning runs. In some regions most of the action occurs in early morning and from late afternoon until dark. In other areas the action goes on nearly all day. Those anglers who troll in deep water for white shad take fish at a slower but more consistent rate.

Favored lures

The majority of shad lures are made with tapered bodies in weights ranging from about a quarter ounce down to less than one-eighth ounce (even less for fly-rod lures). They are colored with red heads; white bodies; and red, white, or yellow tails made of either feathers or impala hair. They can be as simple as a split-shot clinched onto the shank of a hook near the eye with some hair or feathers tied to the shank and a daub of red lacquer applied to the split-shot.

Most shad lures used now are made either by fishermen themselves or by small manufacturers set up to do nothing but that, on a seasonal basis and usually as a part-time occupation.

Many manufactured shad lures are cast in aluminum molds from such low-melting-point metals as Cerrobend or Cerromatrix, which melt in boiling water. Using these metals, it is possible to mold the hair or feathers into the lures without burning them. This eliminates the need for tying the tails on after casting. Commercially made shad-lure molds are available on the tackle market. Considering the high rate of loss in shad-fishing lures, such molds are a worthy investment.

Spinning lines used for shad fishing should be tested for residual strength after each trip. Because shad put up an active, frequently violent fight for their freedom, spinning lines usually are stretched to their test limits and often beyond. Once stretched to a certain point, most monofilament lines will lose some of their test strength. I replace my shad-fishing line every year, and some years I have done so in midseason. Four-pound test spinning line is about right for hickory shad; six will fill the bill for white shad.

Because both species of shad have soft mouths, they must be played, or fought, with a light drag setting to prevent pulling the hooks out.

Rated as the poor man's salmon, shad give a good aerial fight when hooked on light tackle.

A popular practice that has appeared since the decrease in shad populations is to return unharmed all shad the angler does not intend to eat or otherwise use. Actually, many shad fishermen do not like to eat either the bony white shad or the even more bony hickory shad. In some regions the species has been made a game fish and is protected by creel limits. It will help a little to return to the water all those not intended for use. By so doing we may extend the time left to us in this sportiest of all light-tackle fishing.

Chapter six

The pike family

Among freshwater game fish, none can match the family *Esox,* the pike family, for its voraciousness.

Though the lineage includes five recognized species, crossbreeding is not uncommon in some waters of their combined range. Because of the tendency to crossbreed, positive identification often is difficult. But in most cases of record, in a cross between two species the largest and strongest will prevail. For the angler whose interests are limited to catching them, most crosses go unnoticed.

The five species are: chain pickerel (*Esox niger*), grass pickerel (*Esox vermiculatus*), redfin pickerel (*Esox americanus*), northern pike (*Esox lucius*) and muskellunge (*Esox masquinongy*). Of these five, the most popular among anglers are the chain pickerel, the northern pike, and the muskellunge.

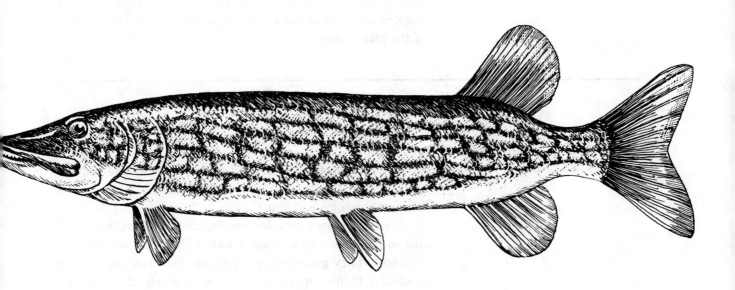

CHAIN PICKEREL

Esox niger

World record
9 pounds, 6 ounces

Taken in
Homerville, Georgia
February 1961

The chain pickerel is distinguished from its relatives by horizontal, chainlike markings on its sides and a bronze-green back.

The northern pike has a profusion of spots on its sides against a background coloration of dark green similar to the color of an olive.

The muskellunge can be identified, usually, by the vertical bars on its sides. However, known subspecies, believed to be geographic variations rather than real subspecies, often are confusing to the angler because they lack the distinct bars. In such cases size is an aid to positive identification since the muskellunge, or muskie as it is popularly known, is the largest of the pike family.

CHAIN PICKEREL

Of all freshwater game fish used in transplanting and restocking programs, the chain pickerel takes third place in importance only to bass and trout.

Listed among warm-water species, chain pickerel make out fine in the same warm, sluggish waters where largemouth bass fare best. They grow fast, eat any live fish they can capture (including their own young), and are seemingly always willing to strike artificial lures or live minnows and spinners. The characteristic of indiscriminate predation persists with all five members of the pike family.

Most abundant in eastern regions of North America, the chain pickerel's total range initially extended (before transplanting programs) from Florida northward to Nova Scotia and Quebec and in the Mississippi Valley to northeastern Texas, Missouri, and Alabama.

Average weight range is listed as three pounds, but chain pickerel weighing as much as eight pounds have been taken by anglers. A long-standing hook-and-line record is the nine pounder caught in New Jersey in 1957. I have seen several in the eight-pound range taken from Maryland's tidal or brackish Magothy River, which feeds into Chesapeake Bay about midway up the bay's length.

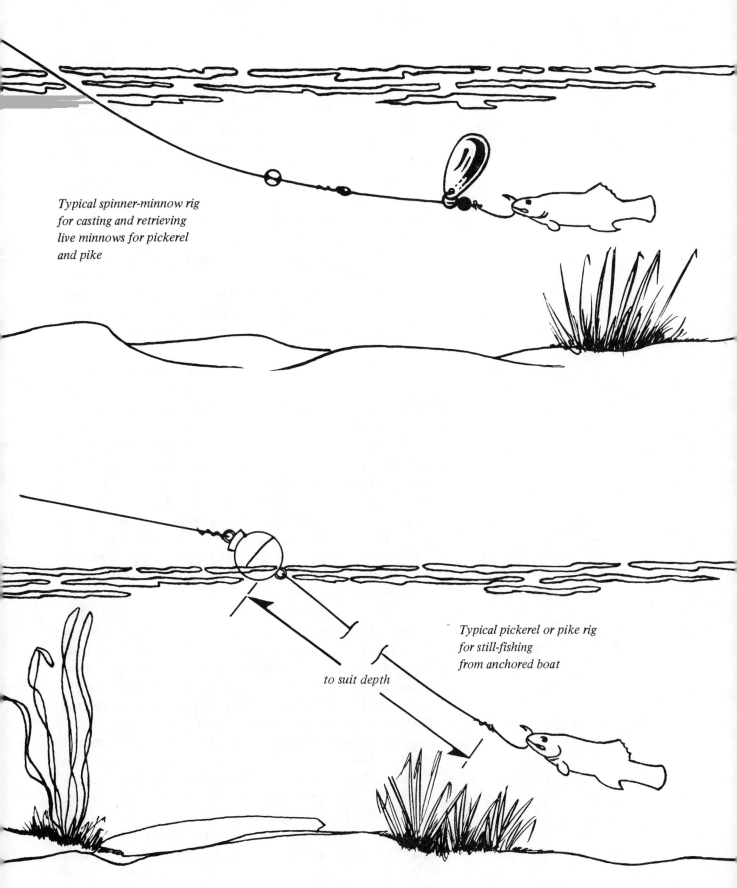

*Typical spinner-minnow rig
for casting and retrieving
live minnows for pickerel
and pike*

*Typical pickerel or pike rig
for still-fishing
from anchored boat*

to suit depth

As a mark of the chain pickerel's tolerance for variations in environment, most of the numerous old millponds on Maryland's eastern shore contain good populations of chain pickerel, as do some of the colder-water lakes in which they have been stocked. It, therefore, is apparent that *Esox niger* is an extremely adaptable sport fish wherever it is found.

None of the pike family builds nests or shows any protective concern whatever for its eggs or young. This precludes the angler taking advantage of extra aggressiveness during the spawning period in the spring months. In fact, the pickerel's level of aggressiveness doesn't seem to change from one end of the year to the other. Even when caught through the ice they show only slightly less activity when hooked.

Gluttons, not gourmets

One of the characteristics that endears all three major members of the pike family to anglers is their uniform willingness to take a wide variety of lures and bait. This is more true of the chain pickerel than of the northern or muskie. I have caught pickerel on everything from fly-rod popping bugs, being cast primarily for bass, to streamer flies, spoons, underwater plugs, large live bull minnows, small bull minnows with spinners attached to the hooks, and even plastic worms.

As a rule, most pickerel seem to prefer a slower-moving bait or lure over offerings that move rapidly or too erratically.

Because all members of the pike family are equipped with sharp teeth, a short wire leader is needed to prevent the loss of terminal tackle—*and* fish.

The sharpness of pickerel teeth has been demonstrated to me several times when I have been casting popping bugs for bass—which, at least in my opinion, precludes using any wire. More times than I can remember I have had pickerel strike popping bugs, make one or two leaps, and disappear with my bugs in their jaws. Oddly, in a majority of such instances the fish have been able somehow to get the bug unhooked, because my bugs often popped up to the surface again where I could retrieve them.

Using a live minnow and spinner combination with a long-shanked hook sometimes is enough to eliminate the need for wire leaders. Pickerel, especially, take such minnow-spinner combinations most often by hitting the minnow at the head end. This seems to get them solidly hooked, with the long

Game Warden Paul Little checks condition of big northern before releasing it in stocked lake.

shank of the hook and the spinner shaft left outside those well-toothed jaws.

When fishing a popping bug, I have found that the same slow, pop-pause-pop technique that works so well on bass also takes pickerel.

Loners, like the largemouth, pickerel rarely are taken in the same spots where bass have been caught. My impression, based on the fact that I have never caught two pickerel closer than 25 or 30 feet apart, is that pickerel stake out a much larger territory than bass do. I have caught many bass as close to each other as 10 feet.

Pickerel will almost always be found lurking among weed or grass beds in water seldom more than 10 feet deep. The exception to that rule may be found in lakes having enough current to obscure the thermocline and keep the oxygen level in deep water high enough so that the lower depths of water are habitable. Under such circumstances it is not unusual to find pickerel taking trolled lures that probe as deep as 20 to 30 feet.

Pickerel that have been introduced into lakes take on some of the bass habits we have come to expect. For example, depending upon the amount of cover available, pickerel may move into the shallows to feed. If the water among the weed beds is too shallow, they will move out to deeper areas immediately after feeding.

Pickerel preferences

As most predators do, pickerel rarely can resist a choice-looking plug, spoon, or spinner-minnow combination even when presented at their resting depths.

Of the three major members of the pike family, pickerel take any lure more readily when there is a perceptible pause between each movement of the lure. This dart-pause-dart action is imparted by the angler with jerks of the rod tip, which cause a quick dart of the lure, followed by a second or two of inaction as the slack line is taken up.

If I had to rate lures or lure combinations in order of preference based on my own pickerel fishing, first place would go to live minnow and spinner combinations. In second place would be those underwater plugs known as "floating-diving" plugs, the type that will bob to the surface when at rest and will dip under when retrieved. Of all lure types, the floating-

100

*Northerns are released
in lakes wherever suitable waters
are available as part
of nationwide restocking
programs.*

diving models offer more versatility for more varieties of fishing than any other.

Deep-running plugs take third position and surface or top-water plugs fourth position. Though a number of my fishing cronies have had different experiences, I have found that few pickerel are taken on spoons. When there is a profusion of weeds or grass, snaking weedless spoons (those having wire guards on the hooks to prevent snags) through lily-pad beds almost always produces strikes, but losses usually are heavy. Even though weedless spoons rarely get hung up, when a pickerel hits, you can be sure it will try to wrap the line around several tough lily-pad stems to break it.

In shallow water it is not uncommon for pickerel to jump almost as many times as the average bass will jump. Moreover, they seem to try to leap in the air, grab the line, and sever it on their way down. Even when pickerel do not actually bite the line in two, nicks from sharp gillrakers and fins can weaken line strength by half or more. That's when a pound or two of extra line test pays off. My recommendation for line suitable for pickerel fishing is eight-pound test, minimum.

Being shallow-water feeders by preference, the early-morning and late-afternoon hours are best for pickerel fishing. I have never caught a pickerel after dark or before dawn.

Recommended hook sizes for use with live minnows and spinners range from 4/0 up to 6/0. Spinner sizes should be from 0/0 for use with small minnows up to 1/0 for larger minnows. The preferred spinner shape is either willow leaf or Colorado.

NORTHERN PIKE

This cousin of the chain pickerel is bigger, more aggressive, more of a loner, more wary, more voracious, and more difficult to land than *Esox niger.*

Average sizes for northerns range up to about 18 pounds. But specimens weighing over 40 pounds are frequent enough in catch records to warrant gearing up for the larger sizes. Though the northern pike never was native to waters west of the Mississippi, transplantings of the species have spread them

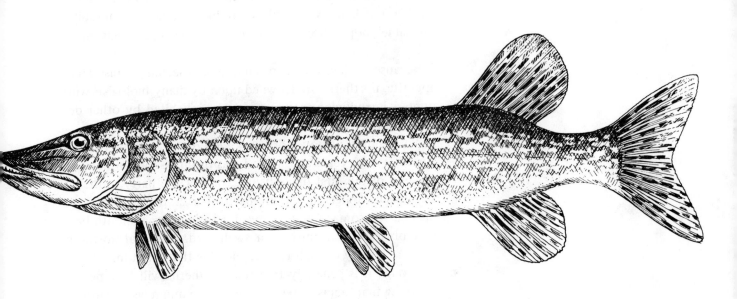

NORTHERN PIKE

Esox lucius

World record
46 pounds, 2 ounces

Taken in
Sacandaga Reservoir, New York
September 1940

over most of the North American continent, as far south as North Carolina.

One of the most vexing problems faced by biologists in transplanting northerns to various lakes is to assure an adequate food supply even during the summer months when natural food supposedly is at a peak. Lack of food has been largely responsible for transplanting failures that have occurred in regions in North America where otherwise suitable waters exist.

Where environmental factors are even close to being compatible, northerns will easily reproduce enough to maintain a "fishable" population—as long as the food supply holds out.

The unneighborly northern

Because of their predacious nature and seemingly insatiable appetite, northerns are frowned upon by many biologists who oppose introducing them into waters inhabited by other desirable game fish.

An example of how northerns feed on other game fish occurred several years ago while I was fishing Georgian Bay. At the end of our first day's fishing, one of the party, noticing an unusual bulge in the stomach of a 22-pound northern, opened its stomach and removed a 3-pound smallmouth bass that obviously had just been swallowed. And that northern still was hungry enough to take the plug that did it in.

Though it is generally true that northerns will take nearly anything that seems to be alive—even live minnows, regardless of their small size—serious pike fishermen offer lures more in keeping with the size of the mouth of northerns in the 10- to 20-pound weight range.

Hooks in the 6/0 to 8/0 size range are preferred; and I have had one set of 8/0 treble hooks straightened out by a big, big northern that got away to bite another day. Fishermens' estimates of fish that get away are never very reliable, mine included, but that fish weighed at least 40 pounds.

It makes good angling sense to go equipped to handle the recordbreakers.

A crony of mine took a 19-pound northern on a live minnow-spinner combination while fishing for pickerel. What's more unbelievable, he landed the fish. Such events are the exceptions that prove the rule. That size lure is not recommended as a standard when fishing for northerns.

From the tank truck with care,
right into the water.
Mortality rate of fish today
is low due to modern aeration
equipment and temperature controls.

105

I am a firm believer in good sportsmanship. But to me, those persons who fish for known big fish with tackle, relatively speaking, in the ultralight category—for example, fishing for white marlin with fly rods or going after northerns with line testing less than 15 pounds—are using more showmanship than sportsmanship. It makes no sense to me to spend the time—and the money—to pursue fish in the northern's size range with tackle built for bass or pickerel. It is a waste of everything and a mark of undeserved low esteem for a worthy antagonist.

Stout casting rods and conventional reels equipped with at least 15-pound test line are my own preferences in northern tackle. There are spinning outfits that also qualify, but they also are in the medium-action saltwater category by other standards. Either way, the important point is to assure having a reliable drag built into the reel and not less than 200 yards of line.

I know at least two expert anglers who probably would scoff at the above tackle recommendations because they have taken big northerns on fly rods. That's okay with me, but it falls into the same slot with taking marlin on fly rods: showmanship instead of sportsmanship.

If you are fishing with a companion, and most of us do, think of how long he would have to wait while you landed such a fish on such basically inadequate tackle.

MUSKELLUNGE

The "muskie," as it is most widely known, is the bullyboy of the pike family. In addition, it is one of the largest of all North American freshwater game fish. Rated by anglers as being considerably less predictable than either the northern or chain pickerel, the muskie is, nevertheless, a prize catch wherever it exists.

Like the northern and pickerel, muskies have been transplanted wherever biologists think they have a chance of surviving. Boulder Junction, Wisconsin, is the accredited "Muskie Capital of the World." Within a 15-mile radius of the small

MUSKELLUNGE

Esox masquinongy

World record
69 pounds, 15 ounces

Taken in
St. Lawrence River, New York
September 1957

town of Boulder Junction there are about 55 lakes with good muskie populations.

Taking all of its characteristics into account, the muskie is the one freshwater fish about which it can almost be said that "he is one downright mean critter." Ascribing emotional response to any wild creature, let alone a cold-blooded one, is not valid. But if it were, the muskie would be number one on the list of fishy curmudgeons. Its actions and reactions proclaim plain bad temper more than sheer appetite.

The appetite that swims like a fish

And its appetite is prodigious. All members of the pike family are known for taking anything alive that they can swallow, but the muskie's diet ranges far wider in this regard than either the northern or pickerel, mainly because of its size and swallowing capacity. Anything alive that attracts its attention during a feeding spree can and has been found in muskie stomachs—including some rather large waterbirds.

As is doubtless true of many wide-ranging fishermen, I have taken muskies that were bigger and fought harder than some of the white marlin I've caught. If the reader concludes from that statement that muskie tackle should be hefty, be assured you are right.

Most muskies are taken by trolling large minnow-spinner combinations composed of suckers, often more than a foot long, and large spinners with equally large hooks, some as big as 12/0. Anglers who prefer casting to trolling will fare about as well as the trollers in any given year of muskie fishing.

Being wholly loners, a big muskie, once found to inhabit a certain area, can be taken by persistence, assuming the angler is using large enough lures or baits to get an old muskie's dander up.

Though a few "specialists" have taken muskies on fly rods, I cannot avoid the temptation to wonder how much part the guide, boat, and motor played in landing such monsters on tackle so inherently delicate. A trophy fish in all respects, muskies do not come to the angler's offerings often enough to risk a whole trip trying to take them on tackle not at all suited to the job.

There are times—and nobody seems to know when or why—when muskies will aggressively rush any bait or lure offered. There are other times when for as long as several weeks in a row they cannot be tempted to strike at anything. These well-known but as yet unexplained "sulk periods" impose all but certain odds against taking a muskie on the first trip. Yet it has been done.

Fishermen who set their sights on taking a muskie need have no worries about finding them. States that can legitimately brag about their muskie fishing do so. They reap a fine harvest of tourist-angler dollars for their efforts.

But knowing that muskies inhabit a certain lake and locating them in that lake are two different matters. Anglers who prefer to find their own muskie haunts in a strange lake had better be prepared to spend a long time hunting for them. It is my conviction that the best muskie guide available should be hired to help shorten the time between strikes. Almost every muskie guide I've met knows where every muskie in his particular lake is "lying up" and can take you from one to another until at last you sink your big treble hooks in a muskie jaw. After that, whether or not you land it is up to you.

Chapter seven

Walleyes

The walleye, often called the walleyed pike, is really a member of the perch family, in fact, one of the most valued members among sport and commercial fishermen alike.

In North America it ranges from the Tennessee and Alabama rivers northwest to the Mackenzie River.

It derives its name largely from the fact that its eyes are opaque, which gives the fish a "walleyed" appearance. But it could as easily be called "bite-you-like-a-dog" and be just as descriptive, for that is precisely what the walleye will do, given the opportunity. Its mouth is equipped with large teeth lining both jaws. Those at the front of the mouth are especially damaging to the unwary angler who tries to pick up a walleye by grasping its lower jaw, as is the practice in picking up bass.

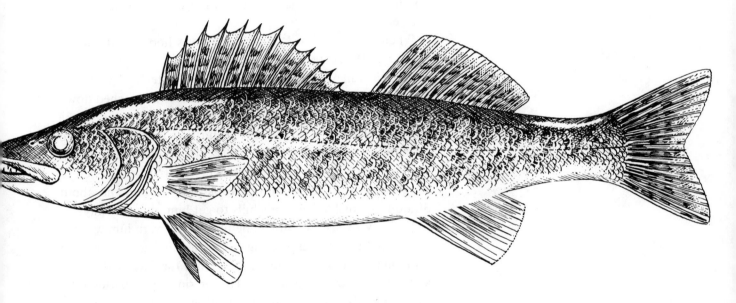

WALLEYE

Stizostedion vitreum

World record
25 pounds

Taken in
Old Hickory Lake, Tennessee
August 1960

A friend of mind named Elwood Goins, now a college professor, got a special bit of education when he caught his first walleye in the Susquehanna River below Conowingo Dam.

Because it was his first real fishing trip, beyond the bent-pin and willow-switch stage that most kids go through, I had rigged him up with a fairly stout plug-casting rod and had tied on a large spoon to ease his initial casting errors. I also admit that the spoon was selected because I didn't really care if he lost it to a snag.

We were casting from the Cecil County shore, and I was about 200 yards downstream from him when he yelped a call for help.

When I got to him I could see he was hooked into something big. It had to be to take that spoon. And soon he had a 19-inch walleye flopping around at the water's edge. Before I could warn him, he made his first mistake: he reached down and grabbed the fish by its lower jaw. The next move came from the walleye, and Elwood found that he couldn't let go because the fish had sunk its front teeth deep into his thumb. Elwood made the second mistake when he frantically tried to sling the fish off his thumb. It took four stitches and about 30 dollars worth of doctor's bills to get him squared away.

My only excuse for not remembering to warn him was the fact that his fish was the biggest walleye I had ever seen at that time. In my home state, Maryland, the record then was a few ounces over six pounds. (It has since been bettered by three pounds. The world-record walleye was a 25-pounder taken in Tennessee in 1960.) We never got around to weighing Elwood's walleye because he ate it, as much out of revenge as hunger.

Some like it cold   The walleye is more abundant and more successful in terms of establishing transplanted populations in the northern sections of the country because it does best in colder waters.

Several years ago I conducted and directed an underwater survey of Conowingo Lake as part of a research project to see how the transplanting of 1500 pounds of walleyes had taken hold. I was personally able to see only about 20 fish, and logged another 10 seen by other scuba divers aiding the survey. All were found in water about 30 feet deep and always under overhanging rock ledges.

112

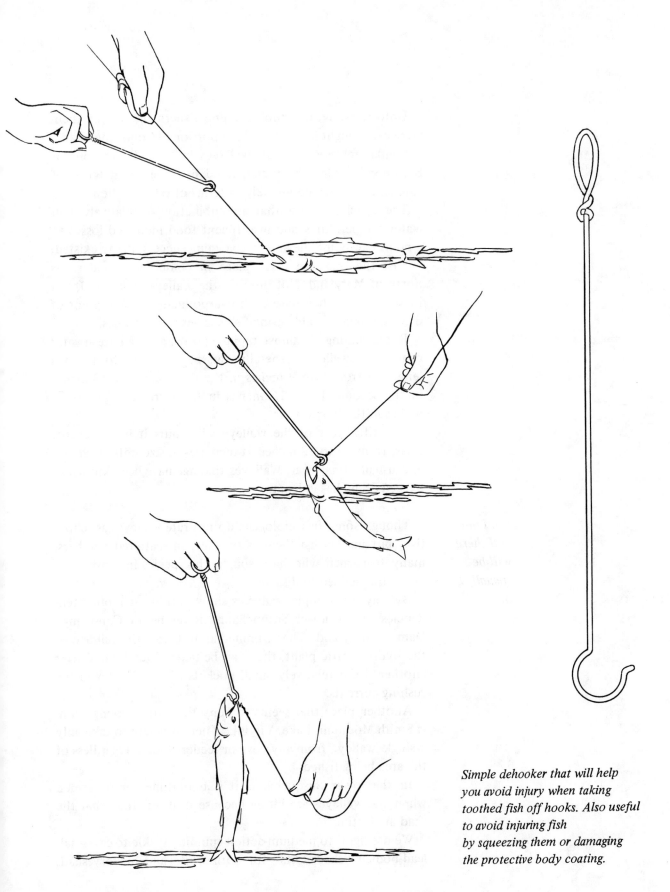

Simple dehooker that will help
you avoid injury when taking
toothed fish off hooks. Also useful
to avoid injuring fish
by squeezing them or damaging
the protective body coating.

Unfortunately for hook-and-line fishermen, few of them were ever caught in the Maryland portion of Conowingo Lake.

Similar releases of adult walleyes in Loch Raven, one of Baltimore's oldest reservoirs, fared little better in terms of catches and failed completely in terms of reproduction.

The conclusion was that a combination of relatively high water temperatures and insufficient food increased losses to a point exceeding the annual spawning success, if any existed.

Just the opposite takes place in colder lakes and rivers north of Maryland. Not only do the walleyes take hold, but in some cases they have even overpopulated to the point of driving other desirable game fish species into declines.

Rated among the most rapidly growing of all freshwater game fish, walleyes generally can be expected to attain a length of from 5 to 9 inches in the first year, 9 to 13 inches in the second, 12 to 16 inches in the third, and 14 to 19 inches in the fourth year.

The fifth year of the walleye's life puts it in the keeper class, from 15 to 22 inches. It increases in size until its eighth and usually final year. Walleyes that age have been known to exceed 28 inches in length.

Find one, and there will be (usually) more

Though some fish biologists do not rate walleyes as school fish, but instead list them as traveling in scattered numbers, many fishermen who have sought the species in most of its range are inclined to disagree.

By way of example, walleyes show definite schooling tendencies in the lower Susquehanna River below Conowingo Dam in Maryland. There, immediately below the tailrace of the hydroelectric plant, they can be taken, literally one after another, from relatively small pockets of quiet water in the rushing currents.

Another place that seems to deny the antischooling claim is Smith Mountain Lake, Virginia. There it is rare to take only a single walleye from any cove or feeder stream, regardless of the area being fished.

In the lower Susquehanna it is boomtime for fishermen when the walleyes are biting because it also is then that the shad are hitting.

We use light- to medium-action spinning tackle to cast small lead-bodied "shad darts" for both white and hickory shad.

Then, for those who want to stay after sundown it is a simple case of lip-hooking a bull minnow on the shad dart and you are fishing for walleyes.

The action usually begins in earnest about mid-April, but walleyes have been caught there and at other nearby locations as early as mid-March. By June walleyes are difficult to take by any means. It is believed that the food supply in the river, which includes a heavy run of gudgeons in addition to the normal supply of minnows and crawfish, is so great that the fish need not take anything that looks at all unreal.

One of the most unusual characteristics of the walleye is its willingness to travel great distances, as compared to most other freshwater game fish, which migrate very little. Driven by lack of food or whatever else may influence them to start moving, walleyes have been known to travel as much as 150 miles in less than a month.

I have found the hours of late afternoon and early evening after sunset to be best for walleye fishing. This seems to be due to sun-shyness, because walleyes will feed actively all day long when it is dark and cloudy or when the water is roiled by rains.

They seem to prefer lying in deep water during most of the high-sun hours of the day. Consequently, where lakes and rivers offer sufficient oxygen at deeper levels they can be taken by trolling slowly near bottom with minnow-baited spinners.

Not until the evening hours do walleyes come inshore to feed in the shallows within casting distance of shore. When walleyes do move inshore to feed, they will then take a variety of small spinning lures that seem to represent live minnows, their principal diet.

Though I have taken a few walleyes on a fly rod with large, bass-size streamers, I am convinced that the best tackle to use for them is either medium-action spinning gear or light-action plug-casting tackle.

WALLEYE TACKLE

115

Listed as minnow feeders, walleyes are in all respects preda-tory. Plugs big enough to attract largemouth bass may be a bit too much for average-size walleyes, but the 19-incher taken by Elwood Goins struck a spoon that was at least 9 inches long, bolstering the theory that big lures take big fish.

In my own experience at catching walleyes I have found them most often and most abundant where there are rocky ledges in 10 to 20 feet of water. Conversely, I have never caught a walleye where there were grass beds or other heavy growths of underwater vegetation.

In strange lakes or rivers known to host populations of walleyes, I prefer to troll deep for them until I locate a school. Then, when possible, I stop and rig up with minnow-spinner combinations with enough split-shot added a foot or two up the line to assure getting down where the fish are.

Plugging
for walleyes

Deep-running plugs, especially those that are floating-diving, are best for probing the depths of lakes after walleyes. The floating-diving variety is preferred because they can more often be freed if the diving lip gets snagged on rocks or other bottom obstructions. Regular sinking plugs, also considered to be deep running, are prone to getting hung up on a wide range of snags that seem determined to cost an expensive lure.

Smaller spinning sizes of shallow-running floating-diving plugs are excellent for inshore plugging early in the morning and from late afternoon until dark, at which times walleyes are known to rise out of deep water to feed along shorelines and on midrange shoal areas.

My favorite shallow-running floater-divers are the Rebel and Rapala types. If I had to select only one type of plug for all freshwater fishing it would be that type. Rigged with a dropper-sinker tied on the line or leader at least three feet ahead of the plug, such floater-diver types can be used for deep work or for trolling, with assurance that the plug will be trying to ride high enough off bottom to avoid most plug-stealing snags. With dropper-sinker rigs it is wise to tie the sinker on with light-test monofilament. Then, if the sinker gets snagged you can easily break it free and replace the inex-pensive sinker.

As is true of bass fishing with deep-running plugs, a slow but erratic retrieve is preferred over a steady retrieve.

Using the floating-diving deep runners, you can actually "feel" the plugs across the bottom by allowing slack in the line when the plug-lip gets momentarily hung up. By allowing slack you permit the buoyancy of the plug to lift it out of the crevice or snag. It doesn't always work, of course, but the advantage is significant over any given year's fishing.

Another effective lure that has enjoyed great success among fishermen in the northern end of the walleye range is one called the Plucky Minnow. Distributed now by Garcia Corporation, the Plucky Minnow comes in several sizes, from spinning up to plug-casting heft. The bigger ones probe deep and are easy to manipulate. They are made of a rubberlike material and are jointed to enhance the minnow action.

The only complaint I have with them is the fine-wire French hooks. Three times I have lost big walleyes when those amazingly sharp but less-than-robust hooks straightened out. But I continue to use Pluckies because they continue to take walleyes for me at a rate that more than offsets the complaint.

Except for topwater lures, generally regarded as useless for walleyes, the same plugs and lures that will take bass also will take walleyes.

Walleyes usually are found lurking in water ten or more feet deep, especially near rock outcroppings.

Chapter eight

The sunfishes and crappies

In the category generally known as panfish there are dozens of individual species and subspecies. But to fishermen, the most important and most popular as light-tackle adversaries are the bluegill (*Lepomis macrochirus*), the pumpkinseed (*Lepomis gibbosus*), the black crappie (*Pomoxis nigromaculatus*), and the white crappie (*Pomoxis annularis*).

All four members of the clan listed above are prized—especially by biologists involved in establishing fishable populations of accepted species to help augment other popular game fish—because they all are hardy, quite adaptable to new surroundings within the broad limits of their temperature tolerance, and prolific breeders.

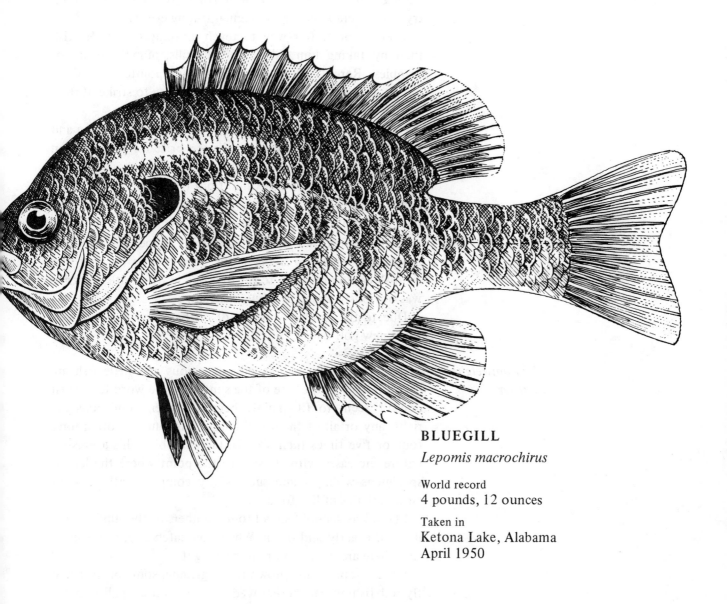

BLUEGILL

Lepomis macrochirus

World record
4 pounds, 12 ounces

Taken in
Ketona Lake, Alabama
April 1950

Having been successfully introduced into suitable waters nearly everywhere in the country, these members of the sunfish family now are available nationwide.

Spring and fall are the most productive times to fish for the sunfishes, but they really are abundantly available nearly year-round, in some places even through the ice. Where ice-fishing is possible in the more northern reaches of the country, winter crappie runs are annual fishing events.

There is no better way to teach a youngster how to fish than by taking him fishing for bluegills, pumpkinseeds, or crappies. Rarely will the novice be disappointed, for these miniature battlers are seemingly ever willing to strike at flies, worms, minnows, or even small plugs.

Once at Smith Mountain Lake, Virginia, Doc Jacobson and I had a bet of three new golf balls as a prize for the first man to catch a fish. (I knew that Doc was talking about the first man to catch a bass, but he didn't put it that precisely).

Figuring to take a big bass, in addition to the first bass, I tied on one of my largest bass-size popping bugs.

The first fish that struck that outsize popper was a bluegill not more than twice as big as the bug. Despite the fact that the fish could not begin to get that bug in its mouth, its strike was obviously aimed at doing just that.

Due to the careless wording of his bet, Doc paid off with three new golf balls.

Bantamweight battlers

Big fish usually are called pugnacious and little fish are called feisty. In the case of the sunfishes, the word feisty just doesn't seem to fit—mainly because, when conditions are right, any or all of them will charge bass plugs or other lures four or five times their size. In fact, the bluegill's aggressive nature increases with its size to the point where the largest specimens willingly and successfully compete with bass for large varieties of live food.

Classed as school fish, all four members of the sunfish family feed eagerly and often. When you catch one, you can be sure there are dozens more to be caught.

Where crappies are known to congregate, some of the finest fly-rod fishing can be enjoyed by tying on a small popping bug and working it with long pauses between pops. Moreover, if there are bluegills or pumpkinseeds lurking around the

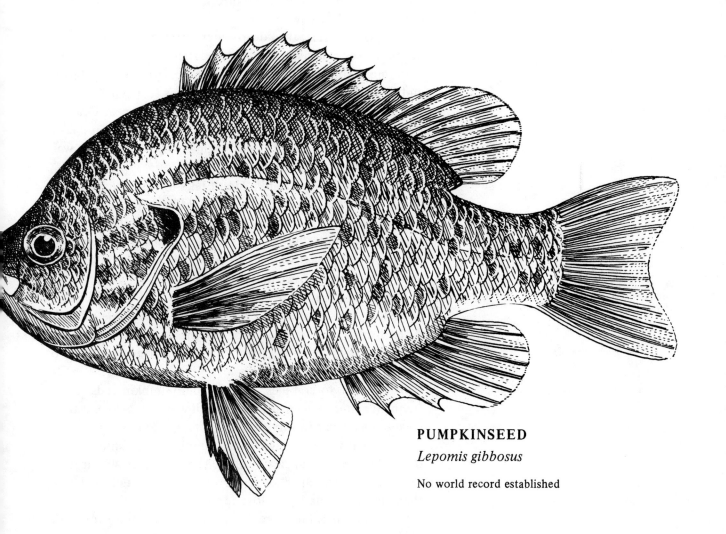

PUMPKINSEED

Lepomis gibbosus

No world record established

edges of the crappie school, be assured that they, too, will take a swipe at your bug, even at the risk of being battered by a big crappie.

*Crappies
go deep*

In waters having tidal flow, crappies are usually found at a deeper level than feeding bluegills and pumpkinseeds are. The latter two will range right up into water so shallow that their dorsals are barely covered.

Crappies will retreat to deep water, often as deep as 30 feet in some lakes, when air temperatures rise during the summer.

In most southern fishing lakes crappies grow fast, large, and in huge numbers. I recall Hank Brenes telling me that his record for one year's catch out of Lochloosa, near Orange, Florida, was a shade over 40 tons of fish. This was in a lake famed for its largemouth bass fishing, which Hank said was mostly for the tourist trade.

"Local boys," said Hank, "don't take to bass much around here because the calicos are so much better eating fish."

In Lochloosa, about four miles long and a mile wide, the crappies concentrated in the middle reaches of ten feet or less depth. The bass were to be found around the edges and among the cypress trees that lined the shores.

The locations known as "crappie holes" are those feeding or resting areas chosen by crappies in which to hide or feed. When fishing strange waters for crappies it is wise to remember exactly where you caught the first fish and be sure to return there on future trips.

In contrast to crappies, bluegills and pumpkinseeds rarely frequent water as deep as 30 feet until winter sets in and they have to go deeper to survive freezing temperatures.

It is usual to see bluegills and pumpkinseeds fanning nests or feeding in crystal-clear water. At such times a delicately delivered fly, streamer, or just a worm-baited hook will take them despite a relatively close approach.

Crappies are a bit more wary. A rule of thumb for both black and white crappies is: if you can see them, they can see you. And chances are they will retreat.

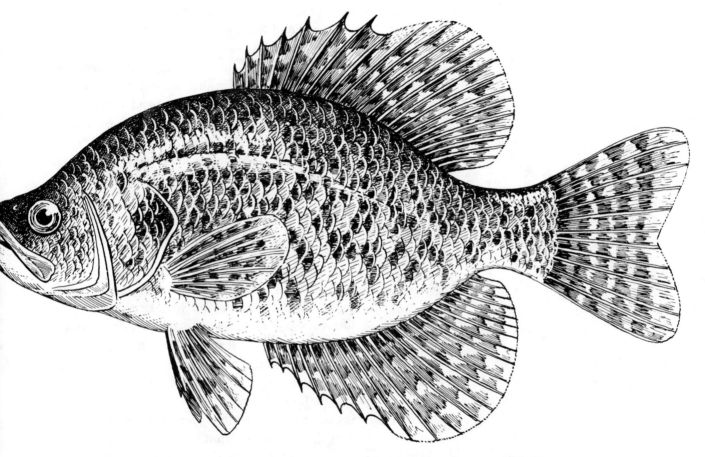

BLACK CRAPPIE

Pomoxis nigromaculatus

World record
5 pounds

Taken in
Santee-Cooper Reservoir, South Carolina
March 1957

**WHAT
WILL THEY HIT?**

For bluegills and pumpkinseeds the most productive fishing method I've ever found is with a fly rod and a bug-type lure made of a small piece of sponge rubber with cut rubber-band legs stuck through it and trimmed off to leave about one-half inch showing on each side.

These homemade offerings should be no larger than one-half inch square in the body, which should be cemented securely to a small fly hook. The rubber-band legs may be inserted by threading one end through the eye of a large needle and pushing the needle through the body at a 45-degree angle. Then a second rubber-band length should be inserted at the opposite angle. Trim these legs off with scissors and the bug is ready to use.

Dry flies also are effective for bluegills and their cousins, but most dry flies are too expensive to use for such fishing if they are trout flies.

As an experiment some years ago, I carved and carefully sanded some really small balsa-wood bug bodies to fit number 12 dry-fly hooks. My idea was to try to take trout on popping bugs, just to see if it could be done. Unfortunately I tried them first on a local trout stream labeled "Flies Only," a restriction I believed would allow my bugs to be used. The state game warden interpreted the regulation otherwise and told me not to use them there.

On my next trip to crappie and bluegill territory I hastened to tie on one of those "illegal" trout bugs. Worked with gentle twitches of the rod tip, bugs that size set crappies and bluegills crazy.

Statistically, more crappies are taken on small live minnows than on flies, streamers, or bugs. But I suspect that the figure might change in the other direction if so many anglers in the south did not fish for them almost year-round with nothing but minnows. In Georgia and Florida, particularly, fishing for "calicos" (as they are called in some areas) is equivalent to a state sport.

When crappie fishing with small live minnows (the smaller the better), the minnows should be hooked either upward through both lips or just under the dorsal fin on the back.

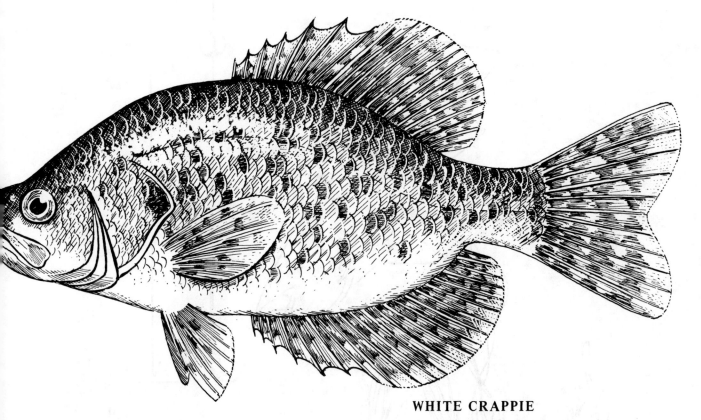

WHITE CRAPPIE

Pomoxis annularis

World record
5 pounds, 3 ounces

Taken in
Enid Dam, Mississippi
July 1957

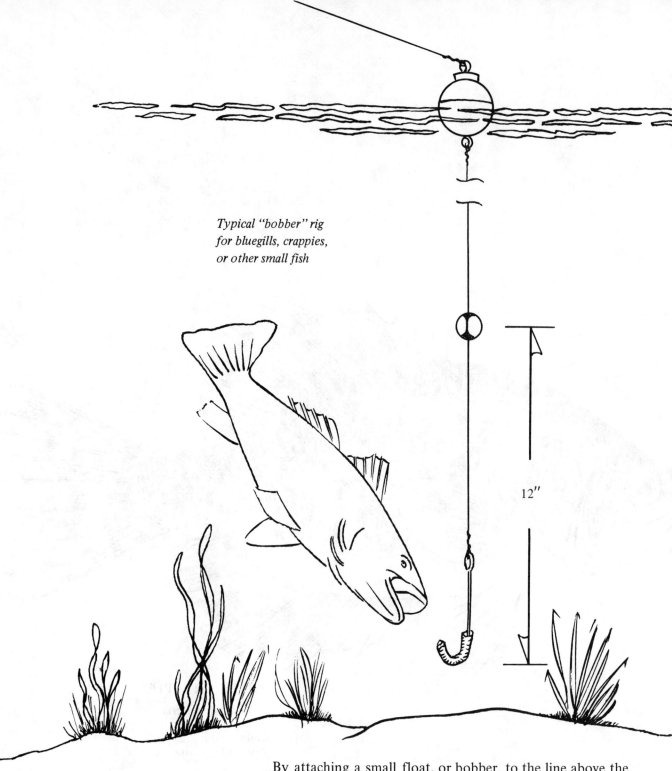

*Typical "bobber" rig
for bluegills, crappies,
or other small fish*

12″

By attaching a small float, or bobber, to the line above the hook you get enough weight to enable easy casting with light spinning tackle. The depth of water should determine how far above the hook to place the bobber. Small minnows should be worked near bottom at grass-bed edges, or just over the tops of grass beds having a foot or two of water above them.

This is not what is commonly called "still fishing," in which the angler waits for the bobber to be pulled under.

126

Instead, it is a method of casting the minnow to likely spots and retrieving it slowly in order to present the bait to as many fish as possible.

In deep water, where bobbers would be impractical, small weights added to the line about two feet above the hook will allow the bait to sink below the depth where crappies are thought to be holding before being slowly retrieved.

Some of the biggest crappies on record have been taken by fishermen using small shad darts with live minnows lip-hooked on them. The weight of the shad darts is enough to take the minnow to any depth desired. With this method the angler should impart some tip action to the baited dart as he slowly reels it in for another cast. Each cast should be reeled in slowly almost to the boat or shoreline. Crappies often follow baits and lures several yards before striking them.

A popular variation of the method is to pinch a piece of split-shot on the shank of a suitable size hook near the hook eye. The split-shot may then be painted red or yellow, or can be used unpainted. With a minnow attached to the hook through its lips the rig provides casting weight and control for whatever depth is desired.

Recommended hook sizes for bluegills, pumpkinseeds, and both of the crappies should be determined by the bait being used.

When using live minnows for crappies, the trick is to use a hook large enough to allow ample bend out of the minnow's lips to assure hooking the crappie. For bluegills and pumpkinseeds, neither of which take minnows very often, hooks ranging in size from a number 10 to a number 14 are preferred. Those sizes would apply for worm fishing as well as for making flies or streamers.

In freshwater hooks, as the number goes up, the size goes down. For example, beginning with number 10, the next smaller size would be number 12 and the next number 14. The smallest hook I have ever seen was a number 22.

Saltwater hook sizes range the opposite way. As the number goes up, so does the size increase. These are scored for size in designations of 1/0, 2/0, on up to more than 12/0.

In areas where crappies, bluegills, and pumpkinseeds are known to reach large sizes (often as large as 2 to 4 pounds for crappies), small spinning lures are effective for all four species.

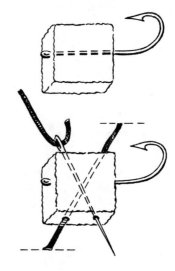

Indestructible sponge rubber bug. Trim shape to suit size of hook being used. Made small enough, the "sponge-bug" is deadly when cast with a fly rod over bluegill shallows.

127

Chapter nine

Yellow perch

I first met Seth Briggs more years ago than either of us likes to talk about—and he predates me by at least 15 years. He was working out his retirement as an elevator operator on the day I went to work for one of the Hearst newspapers. Obviously that was a long time ago, as some readers may conclude from the fact that the elevator actually had a live operator.

As is normal among fishermen, we soon found out that we had the greatest of all common denominators between us: fishing.

Mr. Briggs, as I always called him—and as this is being written I still call him mister—is a yellow perch expert.

Rated as one of the easiest panfish to catch, the yellow perch now abounds nearly everywhere in North America, as

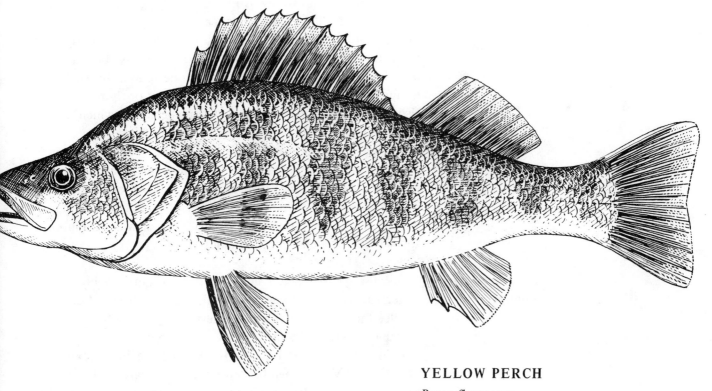

YELLOW PERCH

Perca flavescens

World record
4 pounds, 3½ ounces

Taken in
Bordentown, New Jersey
May 1865

a result of widespread stocking programs initiated by fisheries authorities.

If the yellow ned, as it often is called, is so easy to catch, then what is a "yellow perch expert"?

For one thing, a yellow perch expert is a man who catches more big perch as well as more numbers of perch than any other fisherman you may know. Catching yellow perch is easy. Catching what amounts to trophy-size yellow perch takes a heap of know-how. And that Mr. Briggs has.

One thing that complicates catching big perch: yellow perch reproduce in huge numbers and, where they find the environment really suitable, they school in gross abundance, usually by year-classes—small fish in one school, bigger fish in another school, and so forth. To get a bait or fly to the big fish you must first get it past the smaller ones, which, like most youngsters, are brash and ever eager to feed.

Though some authorities may not agree with my contention, it has been my experience that the larger a yellow perch gets the closer it comes to being more or less a lone wolf. To be sure, they still school, but not like sardines. Instead they will be found inhabiting weed beds or deep areas, much more sparsely distributed than the small fry.

Overpopulation problems

Because yellow perch are extremely prolific, a body of water can easily become overpopulated with them. For example, the Maryland Inland Fisheries Department's sad but solvable experience with them is a case in point.

Using Deep Creek Lake as the site of the initial experiments with yellow perch, department biologists released a small number of adult fish in the 4500-acre western Maryland impoundment. In less than five years there was positive proof that the perch had taken hold with a flourish. In fact, the net samplings taken showed a definite tendency toward stunted growth. Eventually the overpopulation problem required extensive rotenone treatment in selected spawning coves.

Since then a new group of biologists has introduced northern pike, eastern chain pickerel, and walleyes, along with some largemouth and smallmouth bass, to boost the predation factor among the yellow perch. Now the balance has been reestablished and the lake, known as "Maryland's Mountain Playground," is once more a good bet for sport fishing.

130

Catches of yellow perch in the 10- to 12-inch length range indicate that control has been accomplished.

The Deep Creek Lake debacle was a classic goof on the part of those biologists who first recommended that yellow perch be used to bolster fish populations in manmade impoundments.

There are dozens of other examples of similar errors in judgment made during those early days of cut-and-try sport-fisheries management.

In at least three cases I know of the use of gizzard shad as forage fish for game-fish species turned out to be a Pandora's box of problems. In one small bass lake the gizzard shad grew so big and so numerous that they took over the lake. There were shad in that much-abused lake that were bigger than the bass they were supposed to feed. Because it was a small lake, vigorous netting solved the problem after some 45 tons of shad had been removed.

Today, fish-management authorities look upon yellow perch as one answer for ponds that get a lot of fishing pressure or for really large lakes well populated with voracious predators.

The spawning run

In the tidal waters of my home state, Maryland, nearly all feeder streams and rivers host annual runs of yellow perch as they gather to spawn. Similar annual runs of yellow perch occur at many locations around the coastal regions of states that border the oceans. Depending on the local weather pattern, the spawning runs occur in early spring.

When on a fully developed spawn run, perch gather in unbelievable numbers, usually at the mouths of streams. Then, when water temperature is right for their purpose, they move upstream en masse, dropping their eggs as they go.

Yellow perch are free-spawners, that is to say they do not build nests. Instead the eggs are simply deposited in gelatinous masses along with milt from the males.

Depending on water temperatures, the eggs may hatch in from 15 to 20 days. Until they hatch, the globs of egg masses cling to anything underwater sufficiently well rooted to serve as an anchor against the current.

For an angler to catch yellow perch by the dozens during a spawning run is as easy as dropping a baited hook in the water. (Personally I steer shy of the annual spawn runs because, in addition to too many fish, there are too many fishermen lining the banks of all suitable streams.) Even though the majority of perch involved are too engrossed in spawning to feed, there are enough "feeders" to make any trip productive.

PERCH-FISHING TIPS

The best baits for yellow perch include small live minnows, grass shrimp where those little crustaceans are available, bits of angleworm, bits of bloodworm, and streamer flies. My own preference is for the fly rod with small streamer flies or spinner-fly combinations.

In most states there are no daily creel limits because authorities have learned that yellow perch require heavy harvesting to assure population control.

Right after they spawn, yellow perch go on a feeding spree to recoup lost energy. It is then that a streamer or spinner-fly presented to them will do a fine job of taking the bigger perch.

During hot weather the bigger perch retreat to deeper water or to thickly grown weed beds where the direct rays of the sun are blocked. At such times small, weedless spinning lures that will sink in among the weeds will prod big perch into action when nothing else will.

Small live minnows lip-hooked and fished from bobbers or floats also will take perch if the baits are drifted along the edges of weed beds. Such rigs usually are fished with a tight line. Bobbers are used only to keep the live minnows just off bottom.

Except for the spawning period, yellow perch fishing is better during the cool fall months and remains good, even for fishing through the ice, until the next spring brings on a gathering of the clan for the next spawn run.

Biologists, asked to explain why yellow perch do not bite as readily during summer as they do during the cold-weather months, say the abundance of natural foods is one answer.

132

As table fare, yellow perch measure up to all known gourmet standards, as do most of the perch family. One hint, though, if you anticipate a nice catch of yellows: a lot of trouble can be avoided if they are scaled while still wet. After their scales dry out only a little bit, it takes an act of Congress to remove the scales by normal means.

Though some anglers I know prefer to skin their perch or fillet them, my solution to the scaling problem is to soak the fish for an hour or so before trying to scale them. This will not make the scaling job as easy as it would have been had you scaled them as they were caught, but it is a lot better than trying to scale them dry.

The Seth Briggs method of taking big yellow perch includes the use of five cane poles, each rigged with about 20 feet of line, a float and a minnow-baited hook adjusted for depth to suit the water depth he is fishing.

One man's method

Seth Briggs is not a believer in what he calls "fancy-dan fishing tackle." He fans his five cane poles out over the stern of his ancient rowboat and slowly rows along weed beds until he gets a bite—until one of his floats dips under the water. He religiously returns all perch under 12 inches long.

If a favorable breeze is blowing him at the right speed, very slow, he will rest on his oars except to keep the boat on course.

Variations of the Briggs method are just as workable when spinning or fly-fishing tackle is used one pole at a time, or two at a time if there is more than one angler aboard the boat. The key to success in the Briggs way is moving the minnow-baited hooks slowly along the edges of known weed beds.

Where perch and pickerel share the waters, it is common to end a day of so-called perch fishing during the cold months with a limit of pickerel also on the stringer or in the fish bag.

Chapter ten

Striped bass

It is with what I hope the reader will accept as pardonable pride that I, as do most of my angling colleagues in Maryland, look upon Chesapeake Bay as the "striped bass factory" of the whole east coast.

As members of the scientific community, few biologists would make so sweeping an assertion, preferring instead to moderate a bit. To me and my Maryland colleagues, however, the simple facts of Chesapeake Bay's enormity, biologic makeup, and annual production of striped bass are more than adequate to confirm our belief.

From its headwaters at the mouth of the Susquehanna River to Cape Charles, Virginia, where it meets the Atlantic Ocean, Chesapeake Bay is approximately 185 miles long.

134

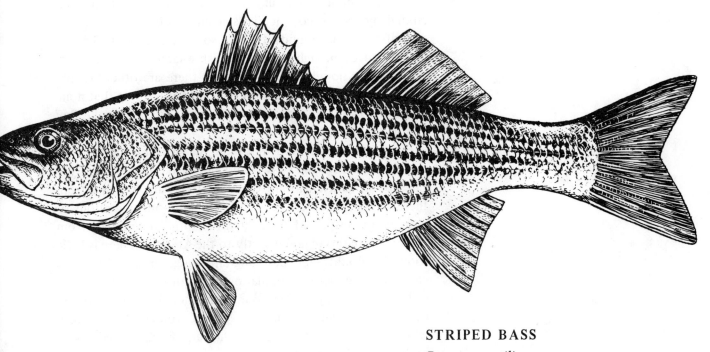

STRIPED BASS

Roccus saxatilis

World record
72 pounds

Taken in
Cuttyhunk, Massachusetts
October 1969

135

Nearly two-thirds of that length is within Maryland's boundaries. The other third is in Virginia. At its widest point the bay spans nearly 20 miles and encompasses nearly 6,000 miles of total tidal shoreline. By any standards, that is—as it has often been called—a huge inland sea.

A relatively shallow body of water, Chesapeake Bay and its maze of rivers, sub-bays, and tidal creeks include thousands of acres of vital wetlands that biologists say are the womb out of which is born the bay's plentiful life.

Within the bay's boundaries there are at least five major and several minor spawning areas that combined produce an annual sports and commercial striped-bass harvest well in excess of 8 million pounds. Despite so large a harvest, the bay still produces enough to help furnish a large part of the east-coast striper population. To be sure, there are other "striper factories" along the Atlantic Coast. But it is a fact that none approaches the size or total productivity of Chesapeake Bay and its tributaries.

Biologists have proved that there is a significant annual migration of big striped bass from Chesapeake Bay through the Chesapeake and Delaware Canal to Delaware Bay and from there to the Atlantic Ocean. Additional in-out migrations of stripers are suspected to occur in significant numbers from the Cape Charles region directly to the Atlantic. There is little room for doubt that these migrants range up and down the east coast augmenting populations from other sources.

The largest population counts are thought to be between Cape Cod to the north and North Carolina to the south, which, of course, takes in Chesapeake Bay, located about midway between the two extremes.

Sport fishing for stripers in Chesapeake Bay begins as early as May and doesn't stop until ice forces the boats to stay in dock, which seldom occurs before February. Among other points, this means that Chesapeake striper fishermen have developed fishing techniques to cover the whole season from spring to winter.

Unlike many other species of game fish, striped bass are as highly prized on the nation's dinner tables as they are by the nation's sport fishermen. Gourmet considerations aside, however, it is the stripers' feeding and fighting habits when hooked that have endeared them to the angling fraternity.

Live grass shrimp can be caught in well-grassed tidal shallows with roller-type shrimp nets. Shrimp are transferred to floating live-boxes after being caught to keep them fresh until used.

The natural range and distribution of striped bass along the Atlantic Coast is from the St. Lawrence River, Canada, southward to the St. Johns River in northern Florida and the many tributaries feeding into the Gulf of Mexico along the coasts of Alabama, Louisiana, and Mississippi.

As the east-coast stripers' fame spread among anglers throughout the country it encouraged authorities to attempt what was then an unheard-of experiment in transplanting saltwater fish.

Between 1879 and 1882 approximately 400 stripers were trapped and transported from the Nevasink River in New Jersey to the coastal waters of California.

The success of that initial transplanting effort is well known. The present range of striped bass on the west coast begins at Oregon in the Coos Bay area, and extends southward to its greatest concentration in San Francisco Bay and the delta region.

By 1935 it was apparent that the "aliens" had indeed taken hold and were reproducing sufficiently well to be called an established fishery. California authorities then declared the striper a game fish, thus protecting the population from commercial fishing pressure. Later regulations also limited the sport-fishing catches to assure an abundant brood stock.

The adaptable striper

The success of striped-bass transplantings to the west coast stimulated deeper and more diversified investigation of the stripers' adaptability. These efforts gained momentum after the discovery that the building of a dam impounding what is now the Santee-Cooper Reservoir in South Carolina had trapped a whole population of stripers. In opposition to all knowledge of the time, the trapped stripers had thrived and reproduced despite being cut off from saltwater.

This was the first known example of stripers breeding in an entirely freshwater environment. After that, it was a foregone conclusion that biologists would attempt many other similar freshwater transplants to see if the conditions of the Santee-Cooper system could be duplicated.

Most of the fish used in the early transplant experiments were taken from the Santee-Cooper Reservoir, on the theory that those particular fish already had adapted to fresh water and were, in some way not yet known, different from other stripers.

Of the numerous freshwater lakes initially selected for striper transplants, few could be called anything but failures. About all the experimenters of that time learned was that it takes more than just clean, fresh water to support striped bass.

Despite the failures that occurred, there were enough notable successes to establish viable fisheries in a number of freshwater impoundments, albeit most fisheries were initially of a put-and-take nature rather than self-sustaining populations.

Smith Mountain Lake, Virginia, is one of the manmade impoundments into which literally millions of striped bass fingerlings were transplanted as part of the nationwide effort to promote landlocked striped bass fishing. The latest regulation I heard for Smith Mountain Lake stripers limited the

*Within the striper's range,
waters around most salt marshes
or wetlands abound in striped bass
during high tide periods
when the fish move inshore
to feed on grass shrimp, minnows,
and soft crabs.*

minimum size to 18 inches. Many have been caught well over that minimum.

Striped-bass successes in such places as Kerr Reservoir on the border between North Carolina and Virginia, Kentucky Lake, part of the TVA chain, Smith Mountain Lake, and others of similar size, have proved that stripers can and will either adapt and reproduce once established or, at the very least, will thrive and grow to enormous sizes even if they do not reproduce.

A notable example of total failure was the transplanting of Santee-Cooper stripers to Loch Raven Reservoir, a part of the Baltimore, Maryland, water supply system. The transplanting not only failed to produce an established population but the fish simply disappeared into the maw of the lake and were seen only once or twice thereafter.

To this day fisheries biologists are not sure what aquatic environmental factors are required to produce a self-sustaining striped-bass population in freshwater impoundments. In the meantime, though, striper spawning and rearing facilities (similar to trout hatcheries) have been built to keep supplying the most likely lakes with fresh transplants until the answers are found.

While scientists have been straining at these problems, fishermen have been exerting even more effort fishing for the species wherever it is found; and with considerably more success for their efforts than has been achieved by their scientific cohorts.

Striped bass are school fish, meaning they live, feed, and reproduce in age groups. When spawning, several males will fertilize the eggs of one female. Stripers are not nestbuilders. Instead, the eggs are free-floating for the brief period it takes them to hatch. The depth of water at which the eggs float is dependent upon the salt content, which biologists say is a common characteristic among anadromous fish (those that live in salt water but return to fresh water to spawn).

As do most true game fish, stripers feed on live prey, consisting of any small forage fish available in sufficient quantity. In Chesapeake Bay and other tidal waters they also feed heavily on soft crabs and soft clams or on bloodworms and similar creatures found in such waters.

Soft clams, or manoes,
are prime striper chumming bait,
especially in Chesapeake Bay,
where the clams are abundant.

With minor variations in terms of local preferences, the most widely accepted methods of fishing for striped bass are trolling, chumming, drift-fishing with live or cut bait, surf casting, jigging, plug casting, and, of late, even fly casting. With rare exception, all of these methods are applied by avid striper fishermen wherever the species is found.

Many charter boats today are equipped with fathometers (depth-finders), used mainly to locate schools of fish.

Trolling: On the basis of numbers, trolling is the most widely used method for catching striped bass throughout their range and transplant-reaches.

Trolling is a method of presenting various types of artificial lures in motion by attaching the lures to lines and leaders which are "trailed" or "trolled" behind a moving boat.

For striped-bass fishing in Chesapeake Bay the favored rig begins with such lures in season as bucktails (local name for jigs) and spoons. These are attached securely to at least 30 feet of monofilament leader material testing at least 30 pounds.

Next in the progression is the sinker, secured with snap swivels to the leader at one end of the sinker. That is known as the in-line-sinker method.

A variation would be to use a drop-sinker at the junction of line and leader. The drop-sinker would normally be attached to one eye of a three-way swivel by about 18 inches of monofilament leader material testing less than the leader attached to the lure. The leader is then secured with a snap swivel to the second eye of the swivel and the line is tied to the third eye.

Drop-sinkers are most frequently used when there is a chance of bottom snags catching the sinker and perhaps causing the loss of an expensive lure. By using 18 inches of light-test material to secure the drop-sinker, the angler is assured that the sinker-leader will break before the line or lure-leader. Some charter captains prefer the drop-sinker method over the in-line-sinker method, regardless of bottom conditions.

bank

dipsey

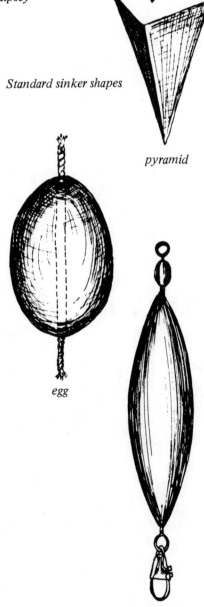

Standard sinker shapes

pyramid

egg

trolling

The main feature of a Chesapeake Bay trolling rig is a stout leader not less than 30 feet long between the lure and the sinker.

Sinker weight varies with water depth and with the size and water resistance of the lures being used. A rule of thumb for selecting the correct sinker weight is to use enough to take the lure as close to bottom as possible without literally dragging it in the mud. Boat speed, usually determined by tidal currents, ranges from slow to very slow, often as little as 900 rpms on the engine tachometer.

Many bay striper fishermen prefer using wire line on their trolling reels because it allows whatever sinker-weight is being used to take the lures deeper than either monofilament or braided lines will, both of which have more water resistance than wire has. The most popular wire lines are those made of either Monel metal or stainless steel.

Trolling for stripers in freshwater lakes differs only slightly in terms of tackle. All factors are geared to suit whatever heft you expect to need to fight the fish. Similar trolling rigs are used in bays, rivers and coastal waters, as well as in lakes.

With any given weight of sinker, the more line that is let out behind the boat the deeper the lure will be in the water.

When there is more than one angler in a trolling boat, it is best if all lines are made of the same material; that is, all wire or all monofilament instead of one of each. This will assure all trolled lures being seen by the fish at the same time.

Chumming: Chumming is the act of dropping chopped or crushed bait overboard into a moving tidal current to attract fish and put them in the mood to feed.

Chumming is done from an anchored boat, and baited hooks are cast into the "chumline," or "slick," that is being carried by the tide.

The key factor in chumming is the need for a moving tide or current to carry and disperse the chum-slick and attract fish. Without a tide you are wasting both the bait and the chum.

Experience has taught us that stripers will quickly detect a chum-slick and will tend to follow it toward its source. Many times in past chumming trips we have caught stripers less than 20 feet behind the stern of the boat.

The best places to chum include off points of land, such as are found at the mouths of bays, rivers, and feeder creeks, and around bridge abutments, oyster beds, and underwater shoals.

In preparing to chum, some bait should be crushed or ground in a meat grinder while a portion should be cut into hook-size chunks. Ground menhaden or alewives, crushed hard crabs, crushed or ground soft clams—all are prime chum bait.

Because the weight usually being cast to the fish in chumming is a generous piece of cut bait, spinning tackle of suitable heft is best to use. Clinch-on sinkers may be added to the line about two feet from the hook to assure getting the baited hooks down where the chum is sinking as it moves with the tide. As tidal flow increases, it may be necessary to add more weight to the line to prevent it from planing up to the surface.

Once stripers take up a feeding position in a chumline, you can cast to them—say, 20 feet or so behind the boat—without waiting for the bait to drift that far on a slack line, which may cause missed strikes.

Assuming a tide is running, a half-hour is time enough to give any chosen location a chance to produce. If there is no response by then, it is best to move to another location.

Most charterboats in Chesapeake Bay use fathometers (depth-finders) to locate schools of fish. Then they anchor up-current from the location and start to ladle chum overboard in modest quantities.

After fish have found the chumline the need for additional chum is reduced to a ladleful every 10 minutes or more. Too

*Spring-run striped bass
will eagerly take live eels,
artificial eels, or chummed
soft clams from an anchored boat
when a tide is running.*

much chum is as bad as not enough, but the leeway is broad in either case.

Much or little, it is important that the frequency of adding chum to the line be enough to keep the interest of the fish. If two or more boats are chumming near each other, which often happens, and if there is an interruption in one chumline, the fish will quickly abandon that line for the other one.

Hook sizes for chumming in tidal waters should be from 4/0 up to 8/0, depending upon the size of stripers known to be available at the time.

Early fishing in tidal striper waters usually produces big fish; in Chesapeake Bay they can range from about 10 pounds to more than 30 pounds. Later in the summer months smaller fish take over after the big stripers have moved to destinations as yet unknown. In the fall the big fish return from their sojourn in limbo and the cycle begins again.

By then, though, there is little chumming bait to be had and the majority of fishermen revert to trolling.

Drift-fishing: As its name implies, drift-fishing is done from a boat drifting with the tide over known feeding areas.

On the theory that live or cut bait that moves with the currents is more natural and, therefore, more attractive to stripers, drift-fishing is a method highly favored by those anglers who do not like the relative lack of action that goes with sitting in a deck chair watching a trolling rod resting in a gunwale rodholder.

Though some anglers fish more than one rod at a time from rodholders when drift-fishing, the majority hold their rods constantly, feeling the bait over the bottom and alert for the softest strike.

Live "pencil eels" (those about 12 inches long) and cut or whole soft or peeler crabs are the most frequently used baits for drift-fishing over striper shoals.

The lines are rigged as for chumming, with hook sizes ranging from 4/0 to 8/0 and clinch-on or small cigar-shaped sinkers attached to the line or leader to get the bait to the fish.

As the boat drifts with the tide, the lines are either cast out or are allowed to feed out until the baits are on or near the bottom. After that the motion of the boat slowly tows the baits along the selected fishing spot.

Drift-fishing usually is good in the same areas normally selected for chumming, with the main difference being that drift-fishing covers more total ground. In effect, drift-fishing is an attempt to drift baits into suspected schools of fish.

Another variation of drift-fishing is defined as "letting the baits drift into known or suspected schools of fish from boats anchored strategically up-current from them." The same rigs and baits are used as for both chumming and the more conventional drift-fishing.

A key point in successful drifting of either type is, Captain Ed Darwin claims, to keep as many baits in the water as possible. This lends an effect similar to chumming. Using soft crabs or peelers for bait, Darwin's mates usually cut whole crabs into four equal pieces, each of which is carefully threaded on a hook. Though these are seemingly large chunks of bait, even a little half-pound striper can and will easily take such offerings. Larger fish want large baits and are more easily held in an area where baiting is generous.

Small fish seldom stay in the same areas being used by feeding stripers, lest they become part of the menu. But if small fish, such as perch or Norfolk spot, do move into your fishing area and begin nibbling the big baits, then it is best to move to another location before the bait is wasted.

*Chumming methods
for striped bass
and bluefish*

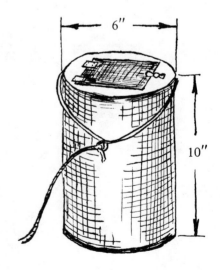

147

Medium- to heavy-action spinning rods and reels are the favored tackle for chumming and both variations of drift-fishing.

Line strength should always be geared to the heft of the rod being used. For example, it would be fruitless to equip a light-action spinning rod with 15- or 20-pound monofilament, because the rod could not stand the pressure that could be applied with that test of line.

Similarly, it would be equally useless to equip a medium- or heavy-action saltwater spinning reel and rod with, say, 4-pound line, since the line then would be too weak to use with the weight built into the rod and reel.

The key word is balance. If the line is balanced in strength with the rod and reel, you can land a big fish with a relatively light outfit. During one of our drift-fishing trips I saw Mike Listorti land a 28½-pound striped bass using a light casting rod and reel equipped with 10-pound line. It took Mike more than 30 minutes to whip that fish, and we had to chase it with the boat several times to let him get some line back on the reel. But that is real sport for those skilled enough to fight and land such monsters.

Leo Bourassa of Smith Mountain Lake regularly lands big stripers with light spinning tackle. Leo even trolls with his light spinning tackle using deep-diving plugs and spoons. He also casts topwater plugs late in the afternoon and early evening, a practice used nearly every place where stripers range in both salt and fresh waters.

Surf casting: Surf casting for stripers obviously is practiced mainly from suitable beaches along the ocean.

There is a theory that big stripers migrate out of Chesapeake Bay and other east-coast spawning areas to range along the Atlantic Coast for the rest of their lives.

The greatest concentration of surf-caught stripers will be found from Assateague Island northward along the Maryland coast up into New England's coastal regions. Though populations fluctuate in both numbers and average size, stripers in the 20- to 40-pound range are every-year occurrences, and in some places are more the norm than smaller fish.

Some November catches from the beaches at Ocean City, Maryland, and adjacent Assateague Island are reported by the

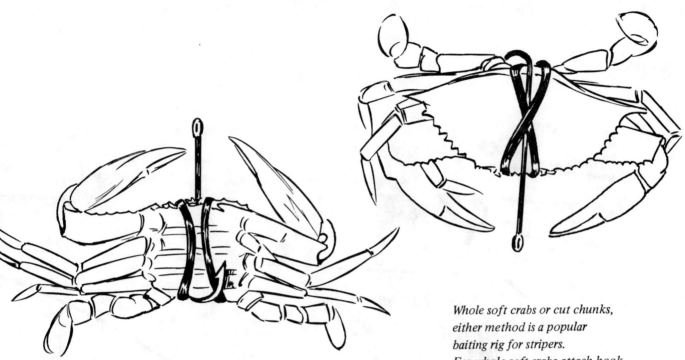

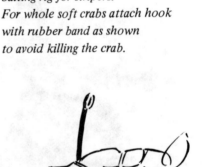

*Whole soft crabs or cut chunks,
either method is a popular
baiting rig for stripers.
For whole soft crabs attach hook
with rubber band as shown
to avoid killing the crab.*

Ocean City Information Bureau: "Rockfish [local name for stripers] over 30 pounds have been taken during the past week by surf fishermen working the beaches here and on Assateague Island." Midsummer and early fall catches of stripers along the east coast are even better.

Though there are a few inland regions where surf-casting tackle is used to take stripers, in most such nonoceanic areas any tackle heavy enough to fight the fish would be as good.

Real surf casting presupposes that the fisherman will need the long-distance casting ability ascribed to either conventional surf-casting tackle or, of late, surf-spinning tackle.

In Maryland, for example, we have been blessed with unusual runs of stripers within easy casting distance of the beaches at Point Lookout, a state park on the lower western shore of Chesapeake Bay. That is an example of some inland surf fishing that more accurately should be called "beach fishing."

Real surf casting, as defined by its devotees, is a method used only from ocean beaches.

Throughout the stripers' east-coast range, and also in the California area where suitable beaches exist, striped bass are taken by surf fishermen using a variety of artificial as well as cut baits.

Block-tin squid, underwater and topwater plugs, and spoons make up the majority of artificial lures used by surf casters after stripers. Bait fishermen use cut mullet, fresh squid, bloodworms, and peeler crabs.

*Even on saltwater spinning tackle
this hefty, a big striper will give
any fisherman a battle before
it can be brought on board.*

The key to successful surf fishing for stripers is long-distance casting. Though there are places where a hundred-foot cast will put the bait in fish, there are more places where a hundred-yard cast would be better. The advent of surf spinning tackle has made the problem of long casts easier, but many surf experts still prefer conventional surf-sticks and spool-type reels.

Jigging, plug casting, fly casting: The common denominator in jigging, plug casting, and fly casting for striped bass is that all three are based on the use of artificial lures.

As the name implies, jigging is done by casting jigs, or bucktails as they are known around Chesapeake Bay, and spinning rods and reels are the most favored tackle.

Plug casting also is practiced, mostly with spinning rods and reels, though a few specialists still prefer regular bait- or plug-casting equipment with conventional spool-type reels.

Fly casting for stripers is a relatively new method developed as an outgrowth of the recent push for saltwater fly-fishing techniques. Fly-casting techniques used for salt water are the same as for fresh water in terms of getting the line, leader, and lure out to the fish.

Saltwater fly-fishing equipment differs from the freshwater models mainly in heft of the rods and the type of reel used. The best saltwater fly reels are equipped with built-in drag mechanisms, something rarely seen in freshwater fly reels. While freshwater fish taken on fly rods seldom if ever are fought from the reel, the potential size of most saltwater fish is enough to demand that they be fought from the reels. Hence the need for a reliable drag mechanism. Also, the "eyes," or guides, on saltwater fly rods should be made of stainless steel to avoid rust, which would ruin the finish of expensive fly lines.

With heavier rods being used it is natural for saltwater fly lines to be heavier to balance the rod-line-reel combination.

In contrast to freshwater flies, saltwater flies usually are much larger and are in the streamer category, tied on stainless steel or Z-nickel hooks to prevent rusting. Popping bugs used for stripers also are larger than those used for bass fishing and require more effort to cast because of their weight and wind resistance.

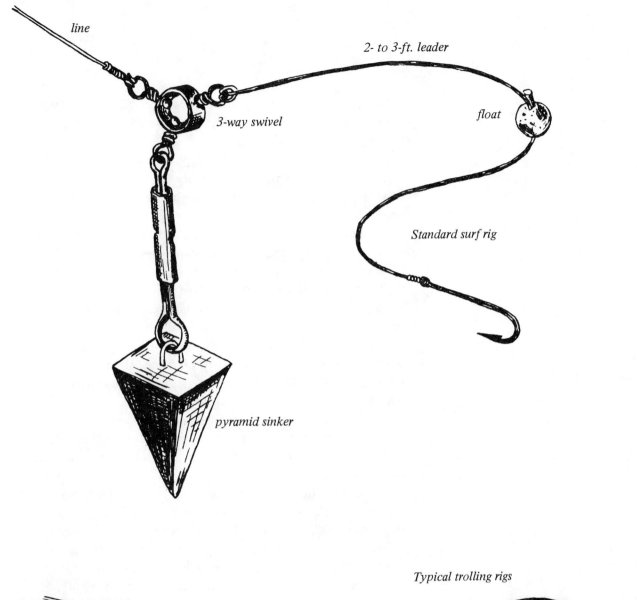

line

2- to 3-ft. leader

3-way swivel

float

Standard surf rig

pyramid sinker

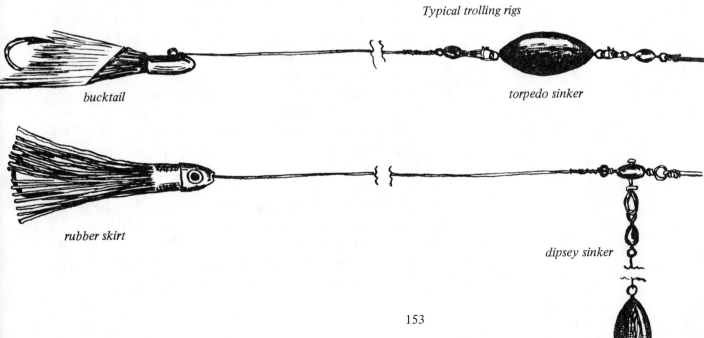

Typical trolling rigs

bucktail

torpedo sinker

rubber skirt

dipsey sinker

153

Most fly and bug fishing for stripers takes place in relatively shallow waters where the fish move in to feed on minnows, worms, crabs, and soft clams.

Barnegat Bay, New Jersey, is a typical example of good fly-fishing water for stripers, especially in the spring months when stripers move upstream to begin their annual spawning activity.

In Chesapeake Bay and other similar waters of the stripers' natural range, fly fishing begins with a search for surface-feeding schools of fish, a frequent occurrence. Experienced fly fishermen seldom attempt to take stripers in deep water.

Plug casting for stripers, as its name implies, involves the use of artificial plugs that simulate bait fish. Casting tackle is either spinning or conventional plug-casting equipment, depending upon the angler's own preference. Most of the conventional plug-casting reels have built-in drag mechanisms, which freshwater models do not have, as a rule.

All metal on saltwater striper-fishing equipment should be of the stainless or noncorrosive type to resist rusting. Reels not proof against such corrosion have been known to last less than one season.

As with fly fishing, most plug-casting success takes place in relatively shallow water, though some of the larger surface plugs can and have drawn attention from fish 10 or more feet below the surface. Again, though, the plug caster's chief aim is to find fish feeding on or near the surface where both top-water and shallow-running underwater plugs can be offered. Plugs are often used by surf casters when the fish are close enough inshore to be reached with average casts.

Of lures favored for striper fishing throughout the fish's natural range, jigs (or bucktails) are the most commonly used, as they have proved the most successful.

Either spinning rods and reels or conventional plug-casting equipment may be used for jigging. Since jigs are relatively heavy (they are primarily lead), casting distances and accuracy are enhanced. The weight allows the angler to work lures either deep or shallow, depending upon the speed of the retrieve and the angle of the rod tip.

Jigs are most effective around underwater obstructions, such as jetties, bridge abutments, ice breakers, and rock piles, and over oyster beds.

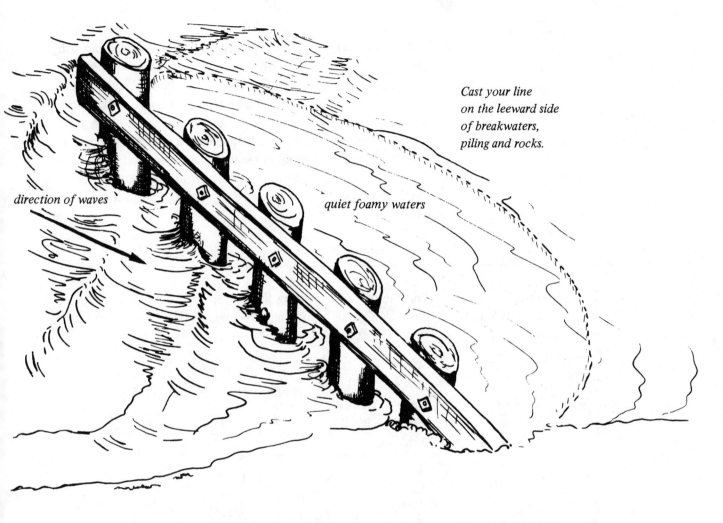

direction of waves

quiet foamy waters

*Cast your line
on the leeward side
of breakwaters,
piling and rocks.*

Successful retrieving speeds vary from day to day and from place to place. Mike Listorti, the most successful jigger I know, uses a moderately slow retrieve all the time with no extra action added by the rod tip. Mike's record of stripers over 15 pounds is nothing short of astonishing.

His formula is the simplest: "Keep the bait in the water and keep it moving." I have seen jiggers take stripers with faster and slower retrieves. I have seen others take fish by jerking the rod tip after each two or three turns of the reel handle. But I have never seen anybody take as many or as big fish as Mike Listorti does every year with his one-speed, no-extra-action retrieve.

Like most other jiggers, Mike favors big jigs (which he makes himself) for big fish. Being a rank optimist, he always assumes the fish will be big. Mostly he is right.

Jetty and bridge fishing tips

155

Although stripers normally congregate in schools, big fish often roam the ocean coastlines as outcasts. Even though it is true that if one big striper is taken from the surf, chances are there are many more, the bigger fish tend to be much more sparsely scattered than smaller fish in the same areas.

Another rule of thumb adhered to by most striper fishermen in the fish's normal range is that a moving tide, either in or out, is essential to success. In nontidal waters the early morning or late afternoon and early evening periods are most productive.

Average weight and length of striped bass by ages

The tabulation following lists "averages" only. It is meant to serve as a guide in judging age and growth rate of striped bass caught in various regions.

age years	length inches	average weight pounds
1	5	no records
2	12	less than 1
3	16	1½–2
4	20	2½–3
5	25	3½–6½
6	28	6¼–10
7	29	10½–14¼
8	32	13¾–18
9	35	18½–24
10	37	22¼–28
11	38	25¼–31¼
12	42	37–38
13	44	40–42
14	48	49–50

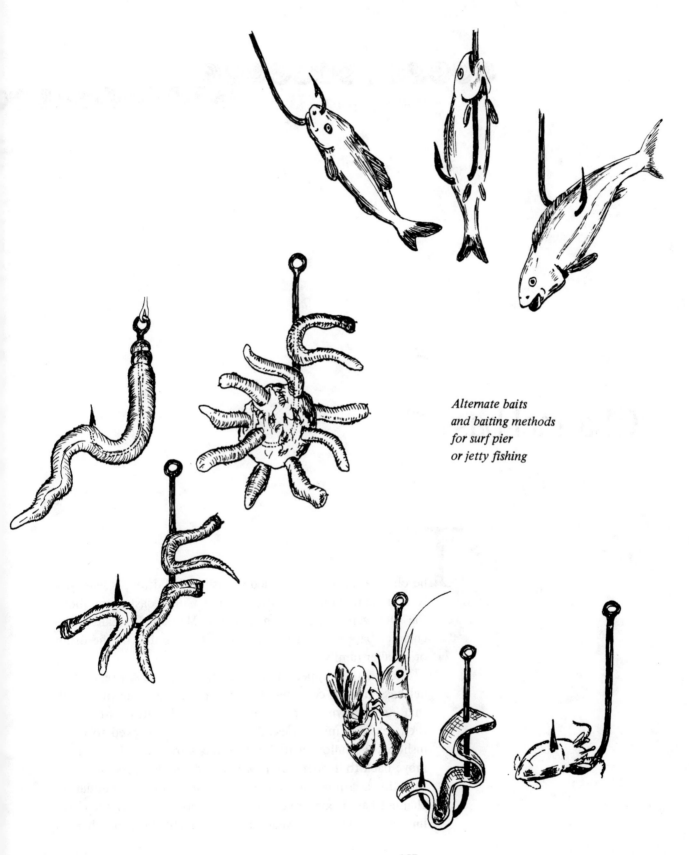

*Alternate baits
and baiting methods
for surf pier
or jetty fishing*

Chapter eleven

Channel bass

The channel bass, often called redfish or red drum, is seasonally abundant along the Atlantic and Gulf Coast from about the Delaware Capes down as far as Mexico. In reality, the channel bass is not a bass at all, but a member of the drum or croaker family.

Though they appear and disappear with the seasons, channel bass are not considered migratory as are some other fish that are known to roam northward and southward during their seasonal migrations. Channel bass are believed to move inshore to shallow water during the warm periods and then move back to deeper waters when cold weather sets in.

With variations in average size and seasonal abundance, channel bass begin appearing as early as March off the Carolina coast. As warm weather moves northward, the channel

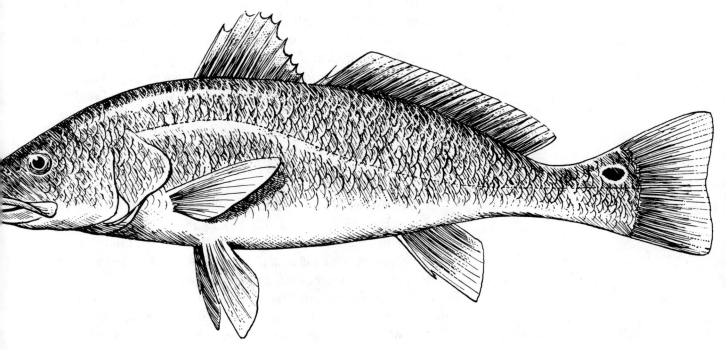

CHANNEL BASS

Sciaenops ocellatus

World record
90 pounds

Taken in
Rodanthe, North Carolina
November 1973

bass begin showing up farther north along the east coast. By June they can be taken through the whole northern end of their range.

Throughout most of its southern range the channel bass can be taken almost year-round, especially in Florida coast locations.

Essentially a school fish, channel bass are highly prized by surf-fishing fans because they willingly range into shallow waters easily reached by surf-casting tackle. Fishermen also take them from small boats that can be maneuvered safely close to ocean beaches when the seas are calm enough to permit close approach.

My own fishing for channel bass has been mostly along the Barrier Islands fronting the Atlantic Coast from Cape Charles, Virginia, northward to and including Assateague Island, plus a few forays down to the Carolinas. I favor the Barrier Islands because it has been there and there only that I have caught and have seen other anglers catch channel bass weighing more than 50 pounds.

One December I was fishing in the Florida Keys with Lefty Kreh. He pointed out a fish lurking in shallow water and I cast a jig and hooked it. When he netted the fish I didn't really recognize it as a channel bass because I had never seen one that small. It weighed less than five pounds.

This is not to say that big channel bass are caught only along the Barrier Islands. Claude Rogers and Joe Sparrow, two of the best channel-bass fishermen I've ever met, take big ones south of Cape Charles nearly every year. I am sure that in some circles of channel-bass fishermen the Carolinas enjoy as good a reputation as do the Barrier Islands among more northern anglers.

A test of strength

To say merely that channel bass in the 30- to 50-pound weight range are "strong fish" would be a masterpiece of understatement. Taken from a boat, channel bass that size will smash tackle for the unwary fisherman who decides he has fought his quarry long enough and foolishly tightens the drag to "settle the issue."

The same-sized fish hooked in the surf feels about ten times stronger, despite the usually heavier rods, lines, and reels used by surf fishermen.

Striped bass

*Striped bass, a universal favorite among anglers,
offer a wide variety of fishing opportunities.
Smaller sizes provide exciting light tackle sport;
hefty specimens can and usually do strain the best
in tackle and skill.*

Important, too, most striper territory also hosts numerous other species of desirable, if less spectacular, game fish to help augment those inevitable slow periods between tides and to add fishing fun for the younger members of the clan.

Taken by numerous area-favored fishing methods, striped bass are caught by trolling, chumming, drift-fishing, plug and fly casting, bottom fishing, and surf casting.

Bridge abutments and other in-the-water structures are considered prime locations for feeding stripers.

Striped bass rarely feed on a slack tide, preferring instead to feed during the ebb or flood tides when moving currents bring bait to them.

Principal baits and lures: bucktails (called jigs in many locales), spoons, soft crabs, peeler crabs, live eels, grass shrimp, bloodworms, and sea worms.

*The lady blasts off a cast
farther than most men can cast—
a must in many of the best
channel bass areas.*

Little gal, big fish....

The first channel bass I caught struck my mullet-head bait while I was standing on solid sand a good 50 feet from the water. Before I managed to gaff that fish some 45 minutes later I was up to my armpits in the water off Wreck Island—and I had been pulled every foot of the way, much against my will.

Once a big channel bass gets his antagonist into the surf itself where wave action creates shifty footing, the fight can go either way. I saw one lady angler pulled out into the water as far as her waning courage would let her go; then she turned around, shouldered the big surf-stick like a rifle, and began marching to shore. She gained dry land, but I suspect the outcome might have been different had the line held.

One of the strongest surf casters I ever fished with, bar none, was a comely gal named Dolly Lagocki.

When it didn't interfere too much with her own channel-bass fishing among the Barriers, Dolly used to hire out as a guide. And she knew her business, from bait-board to gaff.

One year during the May run of channel bass I was lucky enough to draw Dolly as my fishing companion for the first day of three during which a group of us fished competitively.

Dolly racked up that tournament the first day with a catch of four channel bass that weighed, as I recall, from 50 to 55 pounds each. Male chauvinism took a nosedive that weekend. Moreover, fishing alongside that "mere woman" did nothing for either my own male ego or my score.

CHANNEL-BASS TACKLE

Tackle for taking channel bass from the surf should be restricted to stout surf-sticks and conventional reels equipped with plenty of line in the 30- to 40-pound test range.

I have seen channel bass caught on surf-spinning outfits, and some of them were in the 20- to 40-pound range. But I have never seen anybody using a surf-spinning rig who could cast as far as they could with conventional tackle.

Though I am sure there are some surf-spinning rigs that could make muster, too many are borderline in terms of having sufficient backbone to fight a really big bass. One such rig

*Dolly Lagocki, one of the best
in the channel bass league,
beaches a 44-pounder
at one of the Barrier Islands
north of Cape Charles, Virginia.*

I saw had enough heft to hold the fish but not enough to land it. So the fisherman stood there engaged in what amounted to a dead heat between him and the channel bass for the better part of two hours before the line finally parted when his drag jammed.

Channel bass are not fast fish, but they are dogged and bull-strong. When they take half a mullet and head for deeper water to swallow it they mean to get there. And mostly they do just that.

Once a channel bass realizes it is hooked, you can expect a few jolts transmitted up the line, through the rod, and down your tiring arms as your bass shakes its head or scrubs it in the sand to get rid of the hook. That's when a 40- to 60-pound-test "shock-line" pays off in abrasion resistance.

The shock-line is a length of heavy-test monofilament doubled back on itself to provide two strands instead of one. Double-back shock-lines are made long enough to provide several wraps around the reel spool and still leave enough beyond the rod tip for casting. This not only takes the considerable "shock load" imposed on the line when blasting out a hundred yards or more, it also resists sand abrasion.

The rest of the line on the reel should be of a test strength to balance the heft of the rod being used.

My best channel-bass rod was designed by Claude Rogers and is a fiber-glass model called the Hatteras Heaver. Built to balance with 40-pound-test line, it would be foolish to equip my reel with either 20-pound or 80-pound line.

Don't forget
the essentials

Each type of fishing seems to have its own peculiarities, or angler-hangups. Fly fishermen too often forget to check the delicate points of their fly hooks. Largemouth-bass fishermen often do not remember to check their lines for nicks after taking a few bass.

In channel-bass fishing from the surf the most frequently forgotten item is a bait-cutting board. Did you ever try to cut mullet or spot in half against a soft sand base? And as sure as you leave the bait-board behind, you won't find a driftwood substitute within a mile. (Such items as drinking water, bait-boards, first-aid kits, and extra sinkers and hooks become doubly important when you fish a place, such as the Barrier Islands, where the anglers are taken out to the islands by boat

164

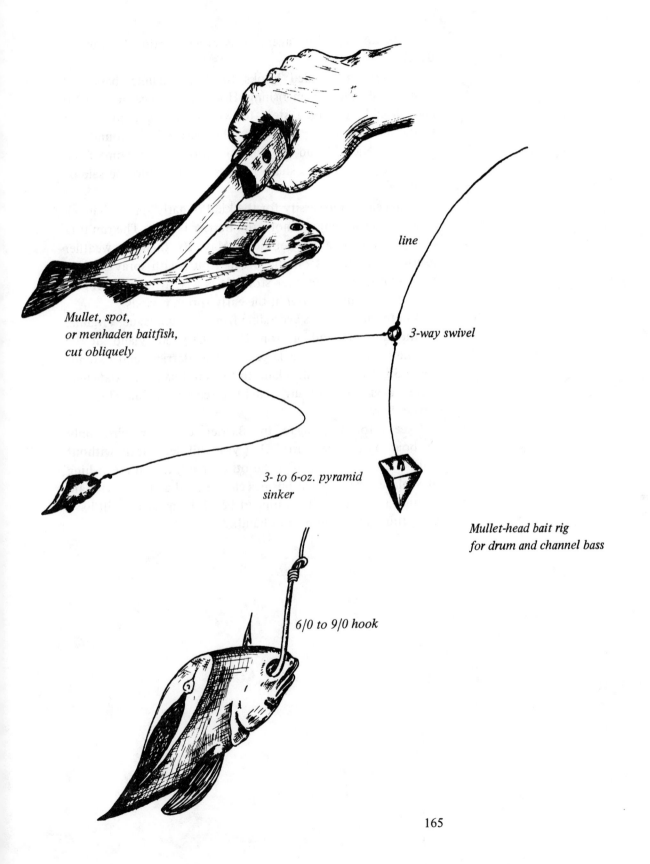

Mullet, spot,
or menhaden baitfish,
cut obliquely

line

3-way swivel

3- to 6-oz. pyramid
sinker

Mullet-head bait rig
for drum and channel bass

6/0 to 9/0 hook

and are not picked up again until an agreed time later in the day.)

I prefer wire-snelled hooks for both channel bass (red drum) and black drum fishing. Hook sizes range up to 12/0 and should be forged steel to withstand the tendency to straighten out under pressure. The best I have found are called "Z-Nickel" and are corrosionproof. They come from the factory with good sharp points, which cannot be said of all large hooks.

Rain gear is a necessity for the kind of early spring channel-bass fishing we enjoy among the Barrier Islands. The run usually gets underway sometime in May. By then the weather ashore is mild. But on the ocean front, with spray soaking your clothes, it is another story. It is wise to carry rain gear at all times, but it is *vital* in the early spring periods.

Assateague Island is accessible from Chincoteague, Virginia, at the southern end or from Ocean City, Maryland, at the northern end. It is the largest of the Barriers and extends some 35 miles from Maryland to the Virginia line. Assateague offers a grab-bag of surf-caught species from May through November.

Except for Assateague, the Barriers can be reached only by boat. You either carry what you will need or do without until the boat returns. On the other hand, if you are fishing at a place where beach buggies can be used and are fortunate enough to own a fully equipped beach buggy, you will have everything you need near at hand.

*Channel bass boats prepare
to leave from Oyster, Virginia,
for run out to Barrier Islands.
In May and again in October
channel bass can be expected
to visit this chain
of small "barriers."*

167

Chapter twelve

Black drum

Like the channel bass (red drum) described in the previous chapter, the black drum is a member of the croaker or drum family, Sciaenidae.

Although ichthyologists list its range as from around Cape Cod southward to Argentina, few hook-and-line catches have ever been recorded north of the New Jersey Capes. Abundant along the coasts of Louisiana and Texas, it also is a favored sport fish in the mouth and lower reaches of Chesapeake Bay and along the Atlantic Coast both north and south of Chesapeake Bay.

Primarily an inshore fish like its cousin, the channel bass, black drum appear and disappear at about the same time—namely, when the water warms to their liking.

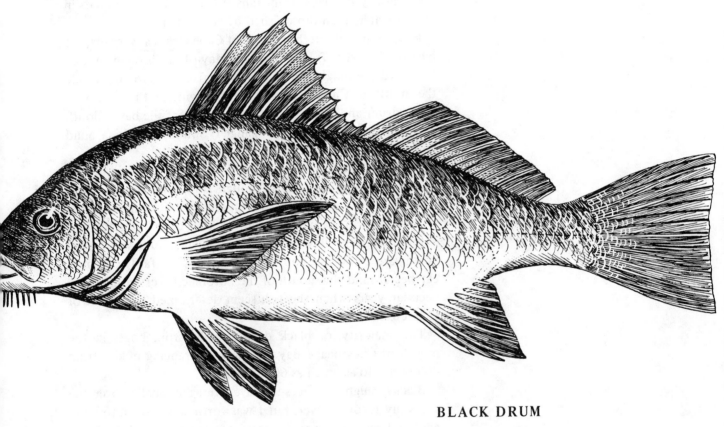

BLACK DRUM

Pogonias cromis

World record
111 pounds

(a two-way tie) Taken in
Cape Charles, Virginia
May 1973, May 1974

Because their feeding habits are virtually the same as the channel bass, blacks are taken on the same tackle and baits used for channel bass where both are present in sufficient abundance to intermingle.

The only difference I have found in fishing techniques is that most channel-bass fishermen opt for surf casting, while the majority of black drum fans fish from anchored boats in deeper waters than those fished by surf fishermen.

Black drum charterboats out of Cape Charles, Virginia, are busy with parties from about mid-May often through June or longer, depending on how long the fish elect to stay inside the mouth of Chesapeake Bay. Other significant runs of both black drum and channel bass occur north of the bay's mouth into the upper reaches of Tangier Sound, mainly around Smith Island and parts of Tangier Island.

The best baits for black drum taken from boats in deeper water are whole sea clams, though some are caught nearly every year on squid and a few on trolled bucktails when the boats make too sharp a turn and the lures drop to the bottom.

In Chesapeake Bay an occasional black drum will forage northward as far as Choptank River. They are fairly common catches around the mouth of the Potomac River during those peculiar years when the fish seem determined to act out of character.

The majority of black drum caught from boats in the mouth of Chesapeake Bay are big ones, ranging in size from 40 pounds to as much as 60 pounds.

Blacks caught in the surf have averaged smaller over the years my records cover, but I was fortunate enough to hook and land two in one evening off Assateague Island that were twins at 55 pounds each.

BLACK-DRUM TACKLE

The best tackle for black-drum fishing from anchored boats begins with lines testing not less than 40 pounds. Rod types favored for this sport fall into the category known as "boat rods": relatively short with plenty of beef in the butt section.

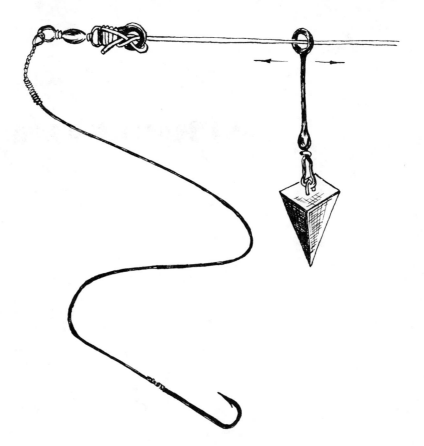

This is not to say that black drum cannot be landed on lighter tackle if all hands aboard the boat are willing to wait out the time consumed fighting an unequally matched battle. More often than not, though, anglers who must wait for one man to land his fish take a dim view of the time lost and the disturbance created among the feeding school of drum.

All hooks used for catching black drum must be snelled with wire to prevent being cut off by the drum's crusher plates or gillrakers.

Despite the claims of some authorities that black drum are mediocre fighters when hooked, many stout fishing rods have been broken trying to land black drum in the 50- to 60-pound weight range.

In my experience, although I must admit to having taken less than a dozen blacks from boats and fewer still from the surf, the fight they put up in the surf is several times more active than from a boat. But, as might be expected of any really big fish, none come to the gaff easily. I know one man who hooked and landed seven blacks in one day, all in the 40- to 55-pound range. It took him nearly a week to recover from strained back and shoulder muscles.

True, they do not jump. Neither do they run very far when they feel the hook. But any man who says black drum do not put up a strong fight has probably never hooked one.

Standard fish-finder rig used by most surf casters

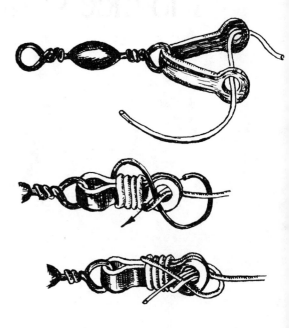

171

Chapter thirteen

Flounders

O f the more than 300 species that make up the flatfish family, all are considered commercially important. A few rate high among sport fishermen.

Because of their wide distribution and the intense angling pressure they draw, only the summer flounder (*Paralichthys dentatus*), also called the northern fluke, and the winter flounder (*Pseudopleuronectes americanus*) have been included here. Generally speaking, fishing methods that will take either the summer or winter flounder also will take many of their cousins as well. Moreover, both are so popular as game fish and as table fare of gourmet quality that few anglers bother to distinguish between them, except by the seasons during which each is abundant.

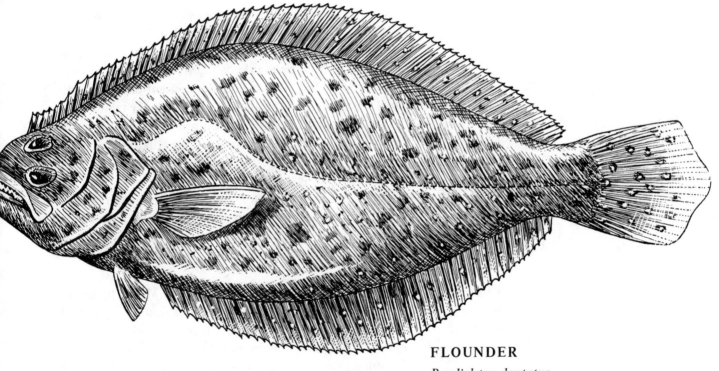

FLOUNDER

Paralichtys dentatus

World record
30 pounds, 12 ounces

Taken in
Vina del Mar, Chile
November 1971

173

Listed among nature's oddities, a flounder begins life looking much like any other young fish. It has an eye on each side of its head and is more or less symmetrical; that is, both sides of its body are the same in markings and coloration.

As the young fish matures, some peculiar changes take place. The skull twists, and one eye begins to migrate to the other side of the head. Finally both eyes are on the same side.

By then the flounder has learned to swim sideways—one of the sides becomes the bottom of the mature fish. In addition, as though aiming for an award, nature added another difference even between these two ocean oddities. One turns out to be "right-handed," the other "left-handed."

The summer flounder, or northern fluke, is left-handed. It lies and swims on its right side, while its eyes are on its left side. Conversely, the winter flounder is right-handed. Both are equally welcome on the angler's line or dinner table.

While the bottom sides of these flipped-over fish turn nearly white, the tops become a brown color that often varies with the color of the bottoms they frequent, this being part of their camouflage system.

By lying flat on sandy bottoms and undulating their bodies, both species can bury themselves in the sand so that only their eyes are exposed. This way they can lie in wait for their prey without being seen.

Where to find them

The summer flounder has a range from Maine to South Carolina on the Atlantic Coast. The winter flounder is known to range along the Atlantic Coast from Labrador south to Georgia. It is the more common of the two species.

Like numerous shoalwater or inshore oceanic species, the main path of the flounder migration is believed to be vertical, from shallow to deeper waters, rather than horizontal, along their coastal range. During the peak of their annual abundance for fishermen flounders are known to invade bays, inlets, and tidal rivers, though large numbers are caught in the ocean at the same periods, many from the surf.

At first glance, an uninitiated angler may be tempted to think that because of its flat appearance the flounder can be reeled in easily, like a shingle or a saucer. The truth is that flounders, on a pound-for-pound basis, put up one of the most vigorous fights of any inshore fish.

Imagine trying to land that shingle or saucer if your line were attached to the center instead of the edge; you will get a faint idea of why a flounder can and often does break strong lines.

Partyboats, or headboats as they are called in some areas, operating out of Atlantic Coast fishing ports drift-fish over likely shoals for the express purpose of putting the patrons in flounder schools. Over the course of any given year the total sport-fishing catch of flounders is astronomical.

Flounders put up a good fight, even when hooked on the fairly heavy tackle that is used aboard partyboats fishing shoals off the coast. In spite of a greater chance of successfully landing a fish with heavy tackle, my own preference in flounder fishing is to drift-fish for them from a small boat using a medium-action saltwater spinning rig equipped with a 10-pound-test line.

As is true of many saltwater game fish, flounders bite best on a moving tide, either in or out, but moving. Slack water at either end of the tidal cycle is virtually a waste of good fishing time for flounders, at least in the waters of my choice. Since their feeding habits are much the same throughout their range, I suspect the same holds true elsewhere.

Prime flounder drift-fishing areas are found in and around the mouths of Chesapeake Bay and Chincoteague Bay, among the Barrier Islands fronting the east coast of Virginia and Maryland, and in most of the bays and inlets along the Delaware and New Jersey Coast.

In those famed flounder regions the favored method is to use outboard-powered rowboats or other types of small craft that will move easily with the tide and are of sufficiently shallow draft to eliminate danger of running aground.

The standard flounder rig (shown on p. 177) is usually baited with live bull minnows (available from bait shops wherever flounders are found) or with cut strips of squid.

At Chincoteague when the tide is incoming we run out, against the tide, all the way to the southern tip of Assateague

FLOUNDER TACKLE AND TECHNIQUES

Island where the ocean has penetrated the barrier reef. Then we kill the motor, drop lines overboard on the side of the boat toward the tidal flow, and start to drift.

As the tide carries the boat, the minnow- or squid-baited rigs are dragged along the bottom where the fish are most often found.

Depending upon where you are fishing, a drift can be as long or as short as you want it to be. Because flounder abundance often shifts in any given area, there will be some times when a complete drift will not pay off as much as at other times.

It's the angler's choice. When the action slows, you can fire up the outboard and run uptide for another drift before you lose the current. This frequently is a wise move when there is a noticeable letup in action on one end or the other of a drift.

A stout chain fish stringer or a cooler box is needed to keep the catch fresh. After losing most of a stringerful of big flounders to a marauding shark one day at Chincoteague, I now opt for a cooler box and crushed ice. Admittedly, that happened only once in many trips along the east-coast range of flounders. But despite the odds, I still prefer a cooler box after that one traumatic experience. You see, I had promised friends enough flounders for a fishfry to which they had invited nearly 20 people. I haven't lived that one down yet.

Don't underestimate "flounder power"

Recommended hook sizes will vary with the size of the fish known to be present. I usually carry a full range of sizes, all snelled with light braided wire to avoid being chopped off by flounder teeth. Rarely have I ever had to use anything smaller than 2/0 or anything larger than 4/0. Several times I have had 2/0 hooks straightened out (and, of course, lost the fish that did it) before changing the rig to 4/0.

If the fish are averaging only a pound or two, then the 2/0 is better. But even if the average size is seemingly small there is always the chance of a stray big one getting hooked. If the angler is using small hooks, he must play that fish with a light drag or he chances losing it to a straightened hook.

When fishing from bridges or fishing piers over flounder waters, it is best to use tackle slightly heavier than regular spinning gear. Such rods and reels would fall into the "bay rod" category, with reels filled with braided line instead of

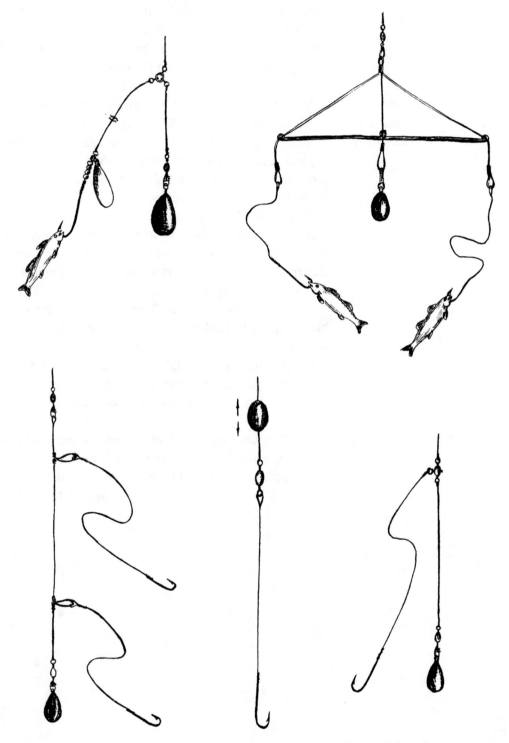

*Optional flounder
and bottom-fishing rigs*

monofilament. The additional strength of such outfits will be needed to reel fish up from the water to the pier or bridge, often a dozen or more feet, before you can be sure they are finally caught. That's no job for light spinning rigs.

Fish fancier's delight

Most flounder territories I have fished have seafood restaurants nearby that specialize in fish dishes. For a treat that cannot be bettered, take your fresh-caught flounder to such a place and ask them to prepare enough for dinner. You'll pay for eating your own fish, to be sure, but it will probably be worth every dollar you spend.

Setting the hook solidly in a flounder's jaw is a prime requisite to avoid last-minute losses of big fish. As the baited flounder-rig drags across the bottom from a drifting boat, the sinker will stir up sand streaks and alert flounders to the live minnows or cut squid.

It is then, usually, that flounders will come out of their hiding spots to strike the bait from behind, in the direction of its travel.

Frequently this results in what feels like a small nibble, since the fish and the bait are going in the same direction. Failure to set the hook hard at such times can mean the loss of fish.

Another important part of flounder fishing is to check the bait frequently to make sure it hasn't been mangled by crabs. This applies to either live minnows or cut bait. Flounders readily detect bait that has been chewed by crabs and will not take it.

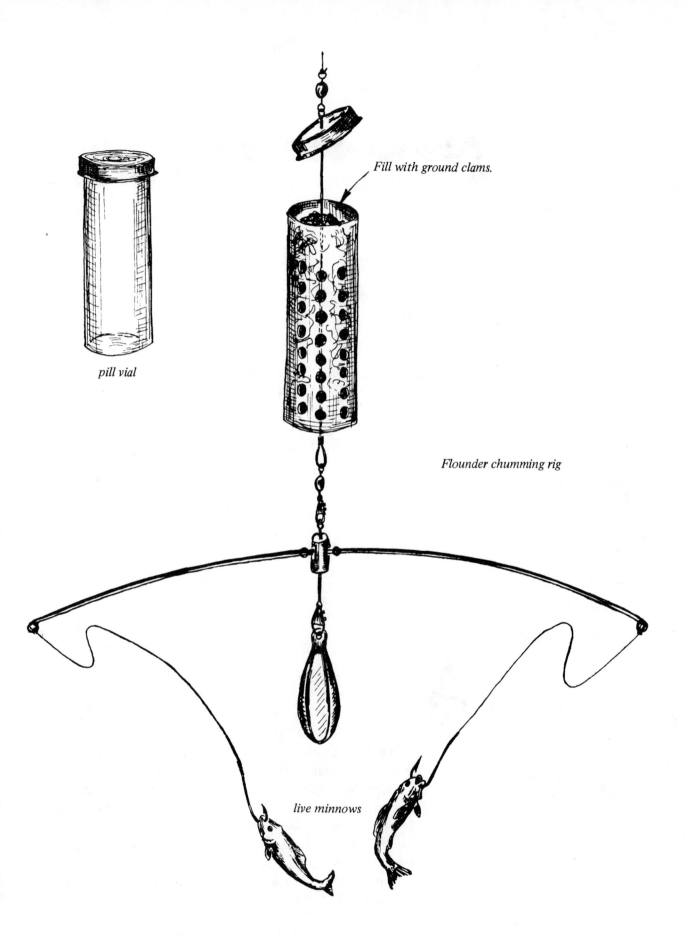

Fill with ground clams.

pill vial

Flounder chumming rig

live minnows

Chapter fourteen

Cobia

As the shape of its body promises, a cobia on anybody's hook and line is a heap of "fishpower," regardless of size.

The first three I hooked made a big dent in my otherwise satisfactory angling reputation among local colleagues.

After the third time that a cobia stripped my reel of line and broke off, my fishing guide, the late Captain Andy Scheible who pioneered cobia fishing in lower Chesapeake Bay, said he had never seen an experienced fisherman get his eye wiped worse than I did.

In those days few Chesapeake Bay fishermen had ever seen a cobia except for pictures.

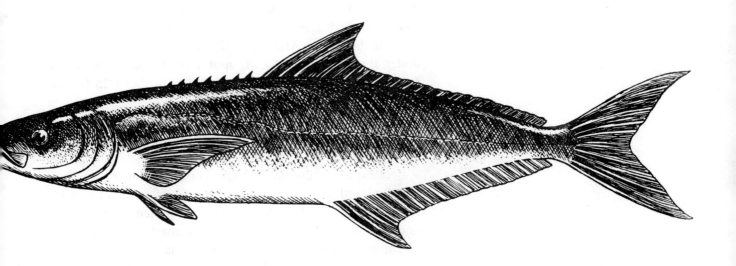

COBIA

Rachycentron canadum

World record
110 pounds, 5 ounces

Taken in
Mombasa, Kenya
September 1964

Captain Andy recommended 30-pound line, at a minimum, and a conventional reel mounted on a rod having not less than a 6-ounce tip. To me those specifications were for marlin fishing by tournament rules that call for what is known as "six-nine" tackle. That is, a 6-ounce tip and a nine-thread line, supposed to test at 27 pounds.

I was convinced that, size be hanged, I could handle them on my favorite medium-action saltwater spinning rig with a reel full of 20-pound-test monofilament. That bit of bullheadedness cost me about 600 yards of expensive mono-line and a badly punctured ego before I took Captain Andy's advice and used one of his "cobia-rods."

We had stopped to catch bait on the way south from the Potomac River to lower Tangier Sound where two shipwrecks were known to harbor cobia. The bait we caught were Norfolk spot, the biggest we could find, and some small sea trout.

Using 9/0 hooks, Andy carefully slipped the point and barb under the dorsal fin of a big spot and advised me to cast it right against the side of the sunken ship in about 25 feet of water.

To make a long story short, I hooked three cobia in less than an hour—and lost all three of them while Andy watched and laughed.

Because a running tide is vital to cobia fishing, by the time I had played out my hand and had switched to one of his rods it was nearly time to quit. We had gotten the tag end of one tide. He had to wait for the next one for another try at teaching me how to hook and land a cobia.

Since that first defeat I have managed to boat a number of the battlers. But in certain angling circles I have never lived down those three losses.

The point I am trying to make is this: never go after cobia with less than six-nine tackle, not if you are going to fish near wrecks or other obstructions which are favored hideouts for that species.

Cobia have a wide natural range. In waters of the western Atlantic, cobia have been taken from the New Jersey Coast south to Brazil. Cobia are thought to be most abundant in the Gulf of Mexico.

Little is known about the cobia's life cycle or its history. About all that is known is when and where it will probably

*Carrying the fight
to the bitter end,
a big cobia resists gaffing.*

show up. We Marylanders know, for example, that cobia usually appear in lower Chesapeake Bay in June, about the middle or the end of the month, and have been caught there as late as mid-September.

In different parts of its range cobia are known by different local names, such as lemonfish, black bonito, crab eater, and sergeantfish. By any name, though, they are all the same on the end of a line.

One treatise on saltwater game fish lists the average size of cobia at 10 to 15 pounds. I have no doubt that cobia in that size range have been caught. But I have never seen one that small. As I recall, the record is over 100 pounds, and 50 to 70 pounders are more normal to the Chesapeake Bay and Cape Charles, Virginia, region. The Maryland record for cobia now is 99 pounds and is not likely to stand very long.

In the Gulf of Mexico the prime months for cobia are May, June, and July, though many years have had catches both earlier and later.

Along the Florida Coast up to about Tampa Bay cobia can be taken almost year-round. In the Gulf off Mobile, Alabama, and Biloxi, Mississippi, charterboats fish for cobia from early spring through the summer months.

Most cobia specialists look for cobia near any floating objects, such as buoys or large pods of floating debris, and around wrecks.

Cobia are not scavengers and will refuse obviously long-dead bait or bait that has been damaged by previous strikes.

COBIA TACKLE

The cobia's normal diet consists of shrimp, crabs, flounders, eels, and such food or forage fish as menhaden, spot, and even sea trout.

Live eels are favored baits for cobia and are fished by hooking them upward through the lips. Eels are relatively easy to keep alive. They are more hardy than other bait species, tough enough to stand casting and still be active under water.

Preferred bait fish are used whole and live if a large enough live-well is part of the boat equipment. If no live-well is

*By the time your cobia
is brought aboard,
you'll know you've been
in a battle.*

aboard, then the bait should be carefully iced to prevent spoilage, which would make it useless for cobia fishing.

Most of the cobia specialists I have fished with prefer their clients to use tackle that they furnish rather than lose too many fish to broken lines and rods.

This is not just another way to glean a tackle rental fee. It is instead the result of long experience in which the majority of first-time cobia fishermen are woefully lacking.

The preferred rigs vary from one locale to another. In Chesapeake Bay, for example, we favor fishing with no additional weight on the line other than the live fish or eel, which is cast and then allowed to sink and swim naturally.

In Mississippi and Louisiana some of the skippers add weight to get the baits down in the deeper cobia waters common to those regions. Still others fish as we do in Chesapeake Bay. It's really a case of hiring a cobia guide and doing what he recommends, at least the first time out.

Among a host of lessons learned the hard way about most saltwater fishing for strong fish, the one that has served me best over the years is to always use forged "Z-Nickel" hooks or other brands of stainless steel hooks whenever the required hook size reaches or exceeds 6/0.

It is difficult for the average angler to believe that large hooks can be straightened out by fighting big fish. Even after losing a few fish for that reason, too many fishermen conclude that they merely had faulty hooks.

Though flaws in tempering or annealing at times have been recorded, it is a rarity for any good hook to fail unless strained beyond its limits.

When fishing for species that are known to be exceptionally strong and hard-fighting, it is unwise to use anything less than the best, or anything less than big enough. The first cobia the reader hooks will amply prove my point, be it a 10-pounder or a 50-pounder.

*Anyone would be proud
of a catch like this!*

Chapter fifteen

Cod

Every time I read statements or hear fisheries biologists refer to cod as nongame fish, I cannot help but recall, vividly, my first encounter with those brutes of the deep.

Captain Ed Brex had taken off from Ocean City, Maryland, to a wreck he knew would produce cod. The cod run in those days was only in its second year of fishable abundance. Prior to that time codfishing off Ocean City was the province of a few commercial boats. Nobody had tried it as a sport-fishing venture.

Though I am not certain that Ed Brex deserves all the credit for starting a new sport-fishing trend, he certainly did a lot to develop it.

Some 35 or 40 frigid fishermen were lined up along the rails of the headboat *Taurus* in mid-February, each with a stout saltwater rod and reel equipped with at least 30-pound line.

Although the breeze that day was a gentle 10 knots, it carried with it flakes of snow as big as silver dollars. The wind-chill index was low enough so that a bottle of bay rum would have at least thickened.

Somehow we all were warm. Well, maybe that's a slight exaggeration. But we were comfortable enough because of the action and excitement so that nobody complained of the cold.

What helped to keep us warm, aside from heavy clothing and thick woolen gloves, was the effort required to hook and land cod in the 20- to 40-pound weight range.

Nongame fish, indeed! If they were any more "gamey," it would take marlin tackle to land them. And even if that *were* the case, be assured that cod-fishing fans would use marlin tackle and brave the worst elements winter could bring— except the high winds that keep the boats safely at their docks.

In the portion of the cod's coastal range that lies off Maryland, the now flourishing sport fishery is only about 15 years old. Whether or not the fish always visited Maryland's offshore waters each year is a subject I've rarely heard discussed. It is enough that we can now depend upon the appearance of cod from about mid-November (in good years) through February.

Essentially a cold-water creature, cod are known to range from Greenland to Cape Hatteras, North Carolina. Some authorities say that cod are not abundant south of New England. From a commercial fishing viewpoint such claims may be accurate, since commercial abundance is measured in tons.

From personal, often bone-chilling, but nonetheless irresistible experience I can attest to excellent sport-fishing abundance from the northern reaches of the New Jersey Coast to the southern reaches of the Maryland Coast.

Cold
and cod
are a team

Although the hook-and-line record among Maryland cod fishermen stands now at 48 pounds, cod have been known to reach 150 or more pounds. Add to the weight the fact that more often than not an experienced cod fisherman will hook two fish before he attempts to land them, and you get a small idea of what kind of grunt-and-groan tactics go along with cod fishing.

Standard two-hook bottom rigs are the most favored terminal tackle for cod fishing. Now and then you may find a man using a three-hook-rig and a line stout enough to handle the combined load of three cod at once.

CODFISH— IMPORTANT IN UNITED STATES HISTORY

The codfish has the distinction of having played a great part in the early history of the United States. Even before the discovery of America, fishermen from northern Europe were ranging into the western Atlantic in search of this most abundant fish.

Prior to the American Revolution and, of course, before refrigeration was available, salting was necessary to preserve fish for any length of time. Codfish were one of the few species of fish that could be salted down without losing too much of their quality. The codfishing and packing industry became a mainstay of the early New England economy, as well as of that of eastern Canada. The fish were salted down in huge quantities for shipment to England and other countries of Europe.

Many stamps of the Canadian province of Newfoundland—in the days when it was an independent country and issued its own stamps—have pictures of codfish on them.

The Massachusetts Colony had a codfish on its state seal. So important was the fish to Massachusetts that a gilded codfish hung between two central columns in the Massachusetts House of Representatives directly opposite the desk of the speaker of the house. Hopefully, it was an imitation of the real thing—although, given the views of many people toward politics and politicians these days, a real one might be thought to be more fitting.

Using hefty bottom rigs, cod are taken most often by anglers using whole sea clams for bait on hooks as big as 8/0 or 9/0. Most cod boats offer rental tackle. The cost of whole sea clams used for bait usually is covered by the fee.

If you grant that the cod is not a spectacular runner when hooked, it still can be said that they give way only after being completely whipped by constant pump-and-reel pressure liberally interspersed with all the line gained being stripped off as they drive hard for the bottom.

By most angling standards, those fish rated as nongame fish can usually be "cranked in" without much action or slippage of the reel-drag. If that is to be the deciding criterion, then cod cannot by any stretch of the imagination be classed as nongame fish. Even the little 10 pounders give a good accounting when hooked on suitable tackle.

Remembering that first cod trip, I can clearly recall the mass excitement that moved my 35 or 40 first-time cod-fishing companions that blustery, snow-ridden day on the *Taurus.*

As the catch increased, the snowfall got thicker and thicker. Inside the first hour of real action the snow was coming down so hard I couldn't see the bow of the boat from my position on the stern rail.

The fish wells Ed Brex had aboard *Taurus* at that time were built to accommodate the usual summer catches of sea bass, porgies, and other regular summer-caught bottom species. As a result, those less-than-adequate boxes soon were crammed with cod. The decks became piled with the overflow, all of which was being rapidly covered with a soft blanket of fluffy snow.

Several times during the peak of the action, which occurred during one whole tide, Captain Brex called out over his "loud-talker" to ask if we had had enough yet. As I recall, nobody even bothered to answer him the first three or four times he asked. To a man, we were all much too busy to bother.

Since those days the cod-fishing fleet out of Ocean City and New Jersey fishing ports has increased at least tenfold in number—and cod fishing has increased a thousandfold in popularity.

What we call "headboats" in Maryland are known as "charterboats" or "partyboats" elsewhere. The distinction between them and other types of charterboats is mainly in the number of anglers allowed per trip.

While U.S. Coast Guard regulations limit the average offshore fishing cruiser to six anglers, a licensed headboat is large enough to accommodate many times that number, including sheltered cabins and more-than-adequate navigation and lifesaving devices.

Because cod fishing uses more rail-room per angler than summer bottom fishing, each captain decides for himself what limit to set on the number of anglers he takes out cod fishing.

Primarily, cod are bottom feeders and are migratory within the limits of their range. In the Jersey Coast region, for example, they begin to appear for hook-and-liners about mid-November; by April there usually isn't a cod to be found. Along Maryland's coast good cod fishing doesn't begin much before mid-December and seldom lasts beyond the first week in March.

In keeping with the nongame-fish rating given the cod by some authorities, I admit there is little or no technique required to hook them when they bite. Aside from a strong heave upward on the rod tip to drive the hook deep into their tough mouths, no special skill is required.

Where the skill and brute strength are needed is in landing them after they are hooked. It gets doubly difficult when you get two cod on at the same time. In what can only be described as "noncooperative cooperation," their combined but uncoordinated efforts can make you think your arms are coming loose at the shoulders, especially when you get two on in the 20-pound bracket.

I have never again had a cod trip that quite matched that first one for success in both size and quantity. On the other hand, neither have I ever again had to endure that kind of weather. In fact, most trips thereafter were warm enough to cause the shedding of some outer layers of clothing.

On the basis of supplying the family table, almost no other sport-fishing activity can promise as much outright profit over and above the cost of the fishing.

Headboat fees along the Atlantic Coast range from about $12 per head to as much as $15, but few trips are logged when the fishermen do not get several times the outlay in honest seafood value.

Codfish cakes, fillets, and other favored preparations keep well in freezers without loss of flavor.

Fresh cod fillets, boiled or simmered until opaque in a fry-pan of salted water, are rated among gourmet dishes. Frozen fillets cooked the same way are only minutely less flavorful.

Because the codfish has exceptionally high food value and lends itself to numerous recipes for cooking and keeping the fillets, few if any are wasted, despite the large numbers taken by anglers during the peak of the season.

Chapter sixteen

Weakfish

The weakfish by any other name is a sea trout. Few other inshore species of ocean fish can match the weakfish when it comes to meriting high regard among sports and commercial fishermen wherever the species or its numerous cousins are found.

As table fare weakfish rate gourmet classification. Even to those of us who rarely order any kind of fish in restaurants, the sea trout is an exception. When caught and cooked fresh from the ocean I submit that there is no finer seafood to be had.

The first weakfish I ever saw was a 10½-pounder caught by an unknown angler from the north jetty at Indian River Inlet on the Delaware Coast. The fisherman who hooked that monster was perched precariously on the slippery, tide-washed

WEAKFISH

Cynoscion regalis

World record
19 pounds, 8 ounces

Taken in
Trinidad, West Indies
April 1962

rocks of the jetty, casting what appeared to be a spinner hook baited with strips of squid. At the time the tide was ripping out of Indian River in a boiling maelstrom of confused currents, all headed for the Atlantic.

Patience—
a necessary
virtue

During the hour-and-a-half that I watched the action I saw the fisherman get hung up on bottom not less than six times. Each time it cost him his terminal tackle. With seeming unlimited patience he reeled in his line, rerigged, and rebaited a new spinner hook. He then cast it to the same place and in the same way that had just cost him a hook, a leader, and a sinker. I judged him to be an amateur. Who else but an inexperienced fisherman would continue to catch rocks and lose rigs so calmly?

Just before I wrote him off as not worth watching, I saw his rod curve alarmingly. When he reared back in the classic hook-setting maneuver I thought he had hooked another rock. Then I noticed that the line was going downcurrent even faster than the tide would have carried it.

There was no doubt that he was hooked onto some kind of a fish—probably a dog shark, I thought. I became even more convinced that it was a shark when the line forged upcurrent as though there wasn't a riptide running. Whatever he had hung into was surely a powerful fish, so I stayed to see the end of the show.

From my vantage point on the highway bridge spanning Indian River I suddenly got a glimpse of a silvery body that swirled once or twice near the surface and dived for the deeps again. That was no shark, but what was it?

The fight lasted at least 30 minutes, during which I had time to wonder about the gentle tactics being used by the fisherman. He acted as if he were fighting a brook trout or a shad. The drag setting on his reel obviously was light, as evidenced by frequent stripping of line and the buzzing of the drag mechanism.

Finally he eased himself down to the lowest rock on the jetty with his gaff at the ready. After a miss or two he succeeded in gaffing the fish and lifting it up out of the water. Minutes later I stood beside him admiring what he called a "tide runner." As he weighed it he explained that it was really a big weakfish, or sea trout.

Since that day many years ago I have fished for weakies at every opportunity. But despite the hours spent in learning the arts and crafts ascribed to expert weakfishermen, and despite catching innumerable fish, I have somehow adroitly managed to avoid catching one anywhere near 10½ pounds.

In fact, that one fish was the only 10½-pounder I have ever seen to this day.

Aside from their value on the table, weakfish are cherished by fishermen because they fight hard and must be played delicately to avoid ripping the hook from their weak mouths, the basis for their common name.

Another plus on the angler's ledger is that weakfish are found in relatively shallow inshore waters that are more or less easily reached by small boats or from shore with light surf-casting gear.

From a practical fishing standpoint the range of the weakfish is from the east coast of Florida northward to the coast of Massachusetts. In my experience the greatest abundance in both numbers and size will be found from about Long Island Sound southward to the Virginia Capes.

The New Jersey coast and its rivers, the Delaware Bay and lower Chesapeake Bay systems, and the Barrier Islands undoubtedly offer the best of all weakfishing during the season when the fish are most abundant.

Although 1974 was a banner year for weakfish in its Atlantic Coast range, and included an early run that got off the mark about the first week in April, for average years good weakfishing is not expected much before the third week in April or the first week in May.

My last trip in Delaware Bay was with New Jerseyites Lou Rodia and Doc Dalling in Doc's 16-foot runabout. With a cooler box supply of squid for bait, we tooled out of Cape May to a shoal known to both Doc and Lou for what they promised would be "a few hours of peak trout action." And that's just what it was.

In less than two hours we had 47 weakfish. The majority of the fish weighed in at four to five pounds, but several 7-pounders were taken that same day by anglers in the small-boat fleet anchored all around us.

The largest weakfish I have caught were taken in Tangier Sound near the town of Crisfield. Tangier Sound is located on the eastern side of lower Chesapeake Bay where the Maryland-Virginia boundary line runs a zig-zag course of about 20 miles from the eastern to the western shore.

There weakfish are known as sea trout and are caught almost exclusively on peeler crab baits or on cut pieces of soft crabs. Both of these baits are plentiful in the Crisfield area; in fact, that community is one of the chief sources of peelers and soft crabs.

The difference between preferred baits from Delaware Bay to Chesapeake Bay can be accounted for by the available natural food supply in each place. One side of Cape May is on the Atlantic Ocean; the other side on Delaware Bay. There, squid would be part of the natural food supply. By contrast, Tangier Sound is much too far from the Atlantic for squid to be abundant, but crabs are everywhere. Weakfish also can be taken on small minnows or spoons and spinners that represent small minnows.

Headboats, or partyboats as some call them, frequently get into schools of weakfish while fishing the shoals off the Atlantic Coast from about the Atlantic Highlands region of the Jersey Coast southward to the Virginia Capes and the Carolinas.

WEAKFISH TACKLE

In terms of tackle preference for weakfish I have found through some rather bitter experience that it doesn't pay to use small hooks, even though the fish in any given school may only be in the 1½- to 2-pound range.

Weakfish have relatively large mouths, as do most predatory species. This means they can take a larger hook than mere body size might indicate. The advantage of large hooks, in the 2/0 to 4/0 size range, is the firmer hold they provide. Because the weakfish has a tender mouth structure, it is almost certain that you will lose fish if they are only lip-hooked or hooked only behind the rim of the mouth.

In terms of rod-and-reel preferences when fighting weakfish, I like a medium-action saltwater spinning rig that has a 5½-foot tip designed with a slow taper to give true parabolic action all the way back to the butt. This affords enough rod

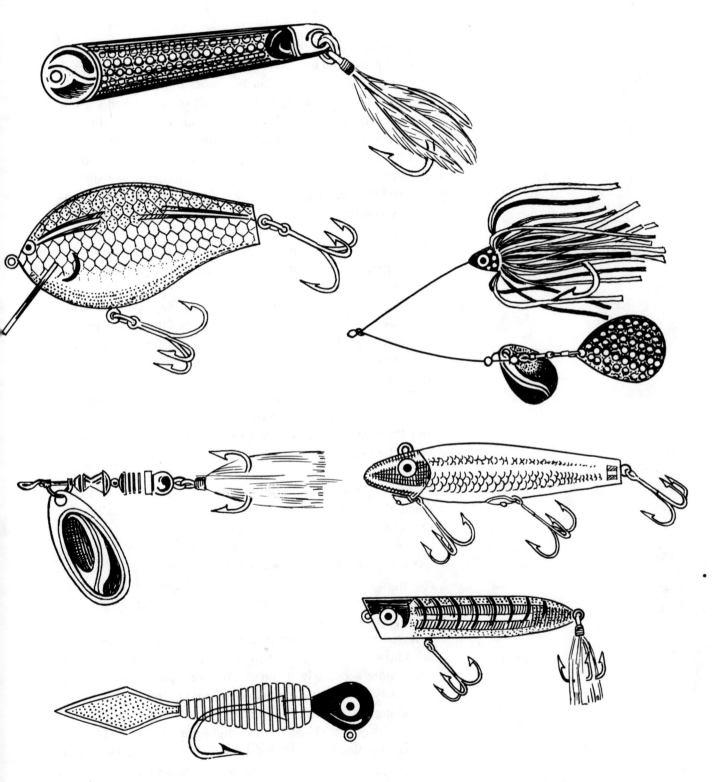

Some typical weakfish lures

strength to tire the biggest trout while assuring enough flex to prevent ripping out the hook.

A steep-tapered rod would be limber only in the upper six or eight inches and then would stiffen up markedly from there down to the butt. If you set a hook too hard with such a rod you will flex it enough to produce a real jolt on the line and hook as the rod arcs to take the pressure. This could rip out a hook before you even get a chance to fight the fish.

A rod with parabolic action flexes more uniformly throughout its length and, therefore, has no hidden strength to impart more power than you expect.

In my opinion the only really efficient use I have found for light tip-action rods is in casting ultralight lures for freshwater fishing of certain types.

Rods can be judged for action by the degree of diameter decrease from the butt up to the tip. The faster the diameter decreases the steeper the taper will be. This in turn will produce more tip-action and less flexing for the whole length of the rod.

The sinker weight that should be used when fishing for weakfish will depend upon two variables: (1) the water depth and the tide; (2) the type of natural food the fish are feeding on at the time.

Generally, more weakfish are taken close to the bottom than at the surface or in the middepths. There will be times when that rule does not apply, but such times will be the exceptions.

A good rule to follow in selecting the best sinker size to use for weakfishing is to select as little weight as possible that will hold bottom against whatever current exists. As the tide changes it may be necessary to add or subtract weight, the main point being to hold bottom.

Rated by many authorities as a "cyclic species," weakfish are known to vary greatly in total population from year to year—more accurately, from one five-year period to the next.

By way of example, the weakfish population was relatively low along the Atlantic Coast range for at least five years, from about 1969 on. Then, about mid-February in 1974, Hal Lyman predicted record numbers of weakfish in 1974 and also a sharp increase in average size. Lyman, publisher of *Salt Water Sportsman* magazine, is a professional fisherman as well as a nabob of the saline angling world. His annual predictions have been averaging more than 90 percent accurate for as long as I can remember. Hal's "crystal gluepot" hit the mark with a vengeance during the 1974 weakfish season.

That also was a peak year in terms of bluefish population, and some believe there is a correlation between blues and weakfish. This is based on the recorded fact that over the past 20 years both species have seemed to share cyclic trends.

Wiping away at least a little bit of the melodramatic hogwash too often attached to fishing for and catching certain species of game fish, weakfish angling owes much of its widespread popularity to the simple fact that when abundant they are rather easy to catch—as are most schooling fish. Fishermen whose egos need a boost will find ample ego reinforcement in weakfishing when the fish are plentiful.

Ego booster for fishermen

The skill involved in catching weakfish is in the landing, not in the hooking. Weakies fight hard, and only an alert angler who knows how to temper his rod and line pressure will land them.

Unfortunately for persons who may wish to take only as many fish as they can eat, releasing weakfish that have been fought hard is of little use. They seldom survive amid the presence of vigilant sharks after being released unless they still have ample energy to zip off immediately.

The only sure way to conserve weakfish, if that appeals, is to stop fishing when you have caught as many as your principles allow. But when the fish are hitting? Well—'tain't likely. Moreover, I seriously doubt that it is either necessary, effective, or even advisable.

The only disadvantage of catching too many weakfish is that they do not hold well in freezers. The best results I have had so far with freezing them have been achieved with a method taught me by Doc Dalling: immerse the cleaned or filleted fish totally in water and freeze the whole package. This can be done in mealsize packs or in flats large enough to hold many meals. All other home-freezing methods I have tried resulted in a loss of taste, unacceptable when compared to fresh-caught weakfish.

201

Chapter seventeen

Bluefish

Many of us in the angling fraternity who have chased bluefish from one end of their range to the other look upon the species with something akin to awe.

Though the idea may not be scientifically verifiable, there is reason to believe that if blues got as big as, for example, marlin, we'd never land one on conventional sport-fishing tackle. Nevertheless, we'd all be more than willing to try.

If there is a flaw anywhere in fishing tackle used to take big bluefish, be assured they will find it. It hasn't happened often in my experience, but I have seen fairly stout trolling rods snapped off like matchsticks by the strobelight speed and violence of a bluefish strike, even with reel drags supposedly set

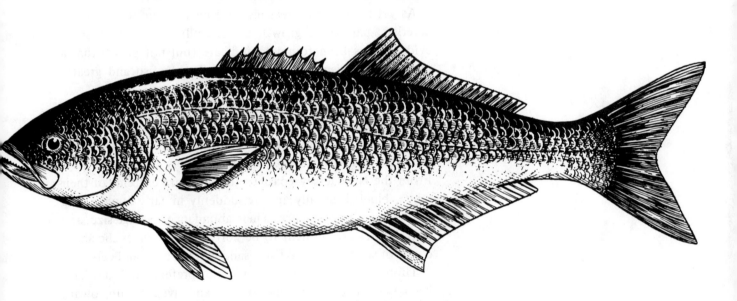

BLUEFISH

Pomatomus saltatrix

World record
31 pounds, 12 ounces

Taken in
Hatteras Inlet, North Carolina
January 1972

to avoid such damage. For sheer strength, the only oceanic game fish I have caught that approaches the bluefish on a pound-for-pound basis is the jack crevalle.

The regular Atlantic Coast range of the bluefish extends from Cape Cod southward through the Gulf of Mexico and as far south as Argentina.

Considered a cyclic fish in both size and abundance, the Atlantic Coast population of bluefish fluctuates over certain periods of years both in numbers and in average size. For example, 1974 probably will be marked in oceanographic records as a peak year following a five-year buildup.

As yet no scientific reasons have been found for this characteristic pattern of growth and reproduction, though some evidence has been found to indicate (but not prove) that a parasitic organism periodically attacks bluefish and greatly reduces their spawning success.

Fishermen in Florida and the Carolinas expect to begin catching bluefish by rod and reel in about mid-April. From the Virginia capes northward along the coastline to Delaware they become available to hook-and-liners about mid-May. From the New Jersey coast to the northern extreme of their range, bluefish usually appear suddenly in early June during most years of abundance. Their abundance, average size, and arrival dates are thought to be correlated to the cyclic abundance of sea trout (weakfish), sand worms, and sand eels.

Though oceanic in both origin and preference, blues have been known to invade coastal bays and rivers far up toward freshwater sources. This invasion usually has been recorded during periods of prolonged drought when the saline content of such waters increases because of lack of rainfall and runoff from drainage areas.

Sport-fishing catches normally are good through summer and into early fall, at which time most populations begin migrating southward again.

As all rules have, that one has exceptions. The migration pattern tends to fluctuate with the abundance-and-size cycle. Because 1974 was an unusual year for bluefish, it will no doubt be used as a gauge against which later bluefish activity will be judged.

The inshore waters of the Maryland, Delaware, and New Jersey coastlines abounded in blues well into November 1974;

*A year when the blues
ran small. During peak years
fish in the 10- to 18- pound range
are common along the
Atlantic Coast.*

bluefish stayed in the lower and middle reaches of Chesapeake Bay until late in November.

In keeping with the size-abundance cycle, blues in 1974 were bigger on the average than at any time during the previous ten years. In Chesapeake Bay that year resident striped bass, for whatever reason, were difficult to catch during what should have been the prime sport-fishing period for that prized species. Some Chesapeake Bay experts believe that the more aggressive and voracious bluefish drove the bay's striper population ahead of them in their northern movement up Chesapeake Bay to the Bay Bridges.

Although scientific knowledge concerning bluefish is sparse at best, sport-fishing efforts directed at the species have been intense and, at times, boldly experimental. Over the years these efforts have produced a number of tried-and-true fishing methods generally practiced throughout the blue's range—offshore, inshore, and in those bays and rivers blessed with annual migrations.

Although the only member of its scientific family, the bluefish has certain traits common to all predators. That some of those traits are more highly developed in the blue than in others only serves to make the species a cherished one among those anglers who especially enjoy the fight to the death waged by every bluefish hooked.

By any reckoning, the bluefish in a feeding frenzy (and that is the only word to describe it) is a vicious, wanton killer inclined to overkilling by about ten to one. In other words, blues frequently kill ten times more than they could possibly eat.

But none goes to waste, for the vigilant sea gull is an almost constant overhead companion of feeding bluefish. Mere minutes after a school of blues have literally destroyed a school of baitfish, eating about one-tenth of their kill, the ever-attendant sea gulls will have tidied up the water.

BLUEFISH FISHING TECHNIQUES

It is the tendency to chop and slash and gulp bits of mangled baitfish that already have been chopped and slashed by their schoolmates that makes bluefish so susceptible to chumming, the most popular of all bluefishing methods.

In addition to chumming, blues also are taken by surf casting, trolling, plug and jig casting, and, in recent years, even fly casting.

While rods, reels, lines, and lures used may vary in each of the above methods, the one common denominator that never should vary is the need for a short length of wire line tied to the hook or lure, without which few blues would ever be landed. Equipped with razor-sharp teeth, blues can and have bitten through even some wire line traces.

More important to the first-time bluefish angler, blues will continue to snap at anything even after being boated. Giving a new meaning to the adage "Once bitten twice shy," an unwary angler who carelessly sticks his fingers or whole hand too close to a seemingly exhausted bluefish may come up more than just "twice shy." Big blues have been known to remove a whole finger joint with surgical precision.

I know one man whose left hand is virtually useless now from the lunging snap of a bluefish thought to be almost dead. It happened on a trip off Ocean City, Maryland, one summer when the fishing was exceptionally fast and furious.

We had boated fish too fast for the mate to get them in the fish-well. My friend reached down to pick up one lifeless looking body from under his feet. Just as he reached for the 10-pound blue, he got a strike and accidentally placed his hand in the fish's mouth. It ended our fishing for the day because we had to take him ashore for medical attention to stop the bleeding. He lost two tendons and suffered weeks of painful infection.

Chumming: There are regions within the bluefish's range where few if any fishermen ever chum. But chumming is rated the number-one bluefishing method because of the quantities of fish caught that way and the number of fishermen who prefer it to all other methods wherever it is practical.

Chumming is the act of dumping or ladling chopped bait overboard for the purpose of attracting game fish and stimulating them to feed. Chumming for bluefish differs from the same method described for striped bass only in the kind of "chum" preferred by both fish and fishermen.

Bluefish chumming boats that operate out of such places as Belmar, Brielle, and Cape May, New Jersey, usually are equipped with large, powerdriven meat grinders adapted to grind chum for their fishing parties. Butterfish and menhaden make up the majority of fish used for both bait and chum. Depending upon the abundance of one or both kinds of baitfish, butterfish may be cut into chunks for the hooks as well as being fed into the meat grinder. Other popular species for chum and bait are Norfolk spot and mullet.

Bluefish show a decided preference for "chum" made of oily fish, such as spot, menhaden, alewives, mullet, and butterfish. The preference is believed to be based upon their diet, which consists mainly of schooling prey as contrasted with, for example, crabs, which do swim but not in schools or at fast speeds. Beyond those preferences, bluefish are known for eating anything alive that is not bigger than they are and often trying to eat a lot of things that do surpass them in size.

As with all chumming techniques, a moving current or tide is essential to carry the chumline to waiting fish. They will, upon discovering the oils and bits of bait coming to them, follow the line toward its source.

Except for the addition of a short trace of wire or a wire-snelled hook, tackle and methods used for bluefish chumming are the same as for striped-bass chumming described in an earlier chapter. But there the similarity ends.

Piscatorial powerhouse

Where a big striped bass in its first run will peel off perhaps 50 yards of line against a moderate drag setting, the same weight bluefish would strip twice that much line off the reel in less than half the time. Then it might slow down.

If the reel drag functions flawlessly, your chances of landing a big bluefish (10 pounds or more) are good. If the drag sticks only a split second at the wrong time, a 10-pound bluefish can break a 20-pound line as if it were sewing cotton.

When hooked and making its initial surging run, the weight of a bluefish has no relation to the size line it can break. Even to veteran bluefishing fans those first runs are awesome demonstrations of sheer horsepower—or perhaps it should more rightly be called "fishpower."

Bluefish should be fought with the rod tip held high, letting the bend of the rod flex and give as the fish pulls and lunges. The high-held rod tip may also provide a split second of leeway to free a sticky drag before the line pops.

Most bluefish chummers fish a drag setting that is just barely enough to set the hook. By so doing they assure extra leeway against sticky drags. They also keep their drags set light to allow hooked fish to swim away from other lines not yet hooked into fighting fish. This is done in an attempt to prevent the hooked fish from tangling all other lines in its fight for freedom.

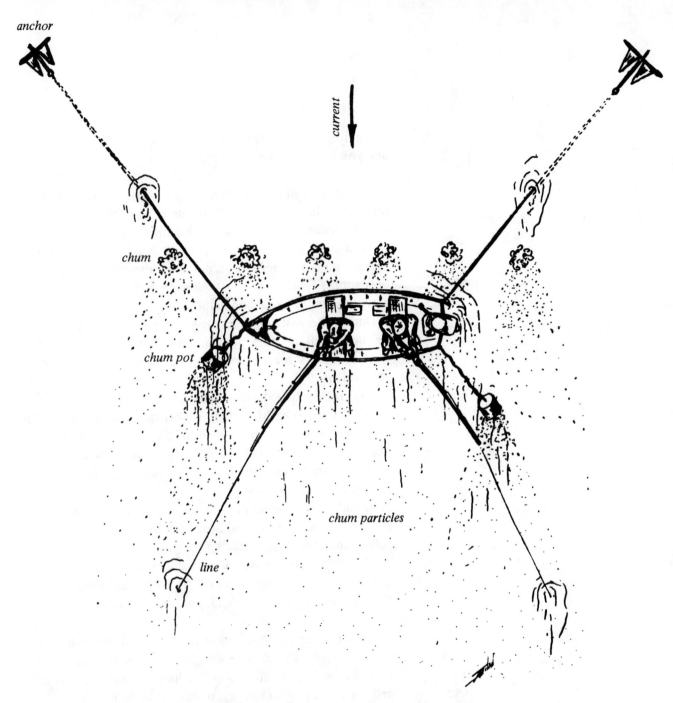

anchor

current

chum

chum pot

chum particles

line

Setting up a chum line

Fishing a light drag setting when chumming from headboats or partyboats with 35 or more other anglers lining the rail is the mark of an experienced bluefish angler.

Failure to fish a suitably light drag will result in massive tangles with other lines as hooked blues on tight drags fight in close to the boat and the other lines. By letting the hooked fish take line out beyond the main chumming area you will assure fewer tangles as the fish fight themselves out in relatively open water. Mates and skippers often give such advice when they know an angler is inexperienced in headboat

209

chumming. If they forget, you can be sure the man whose line you tangle with will fill the gap.

Trolling: Trolling for blues differs markedly from trolling for striped bass. Beginning with lures, bluefish anglers prefer such tradename hardware as the Ragmop, an elongated, multi-hooked representation of (supposedly) an eel. Artificial eels also are on the preferred list, along with spoons and big buck-tails adorned with a red or yellow pork-rind strip, preferably with an extra hook embedded in it.

During the past ten years or so a lure known as the "surgical hose" has become popular, especially among fishermen trolling the inshore waters, rivers, and bays that host bluefish each season.

The trolling lure derives its name from the fact that it originally was made of high-grade rubber hose or tubing used in hospitals for various medical purposes. Since its rise in angler popularity created a solid demand, several manufacturers have produced variations of the originals to augment the extensive homemade models.

In addition to being one of the best bluefish lures known, the rubber tube or surgical hose is all but impervious to blue-fish teeth. And that, alone, is a big plus factor.

The most popular bait for ocean trolling is a lure known as the "Japanese Feather Bait." As with other popular lures, there are many variations, and few are made in Japan.

Troll shallow, troll deep

When trolling for blues, most captains troll faster than they do for stripers. Unless schooling blues are plainly evident, the best approach to trolling is to set half the lines to troll deep and the other half to run just under the surface.

Frequently, bluefish schools will be "layered"; that is, big fish will move close to the bottom and smaller fish close to the surface of the water. By testing the situation with lines set at two different depths you get a chance to see what the deeper water has to offer.

Though some charter skippers use heavy-test monofilament leaders in place of the short wire trace mentioned earlier, I prefer the wire, despite the fact that most blues caught in the ocean seldom get the lure deep enough in their mouths to cut the leader. The loss of one or two really big bluefish because

210

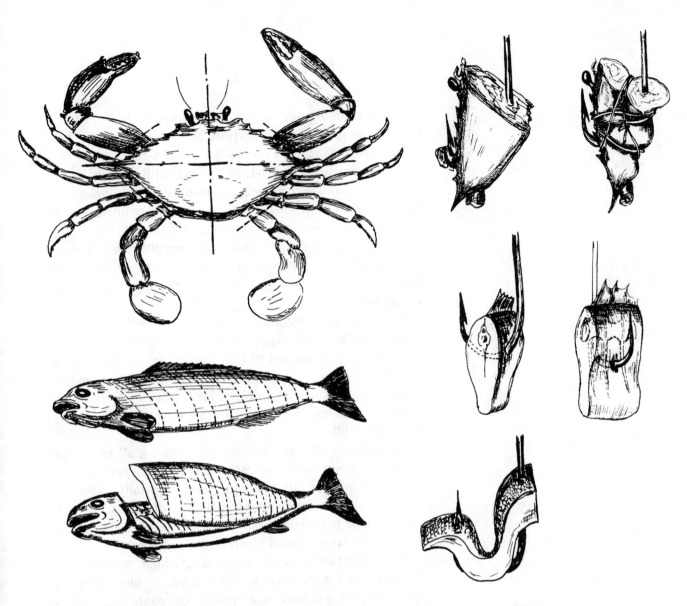

Accepted bait-cutting methods

of cut leaders was enough to convince me of the all-time need for a wire trace at the lure.

Bluefishing from charterboats imposes a few "musts" that I could do without in terms of personal preferences. With up to six anglers aboard a charterboat and the accompanying six lines trolling astern, the first man to hook a fish must fight his quarry while the boat continues to move at a fairly rapid pace. To stop the boat for one man fighting one fish would be an imposition on the other five anglers unless all are agreed beforehand that they want to do it that way. Even then, few charter captains will agree to such arrangements because their reputations are built on how many fish they toss up on the docks each day. And it must be admitted that stopping the boat for one fish will greatly reduce the total catch.

Private boats are not bound by such rules. With compatible fishing colleagues aboard a private boat, the most sport can be had by drawing straws to see which man gets to fight the first fish, which the second, and so on until all have had a turn. That way the boat may be stopped so the angler and the fish can have it out between them. And the difference in sporting aspects is worth considering.

As often happens, more than one fish will strike at a time. If so, then the number-one man and the number-two man take their fighting positions and go to work while their colleagues watch.

To me, at least, fighting a blue from a moving boat is a waste of good bluefish sport. If the tackle is stout enough to hold, then the movement of the boat will drown the bluefish long before it can give a real account of its fighting ability. Many anglers who have caught blues chumming from an anchored boat are reluctant to fight them from a moving boat while trolling.

The majority of charterboats either furnish all tackle for the charter fee or offer adequate tackle and lures for hire.

Trolling from private boats for blues, especially in coastal waters, imposes a need for a number of decisions. Not the least of these is to determine the most desirable and efficient method of getting hooked bluefish aboard the boat.

Where the heft of most rented charterboat tackle allows the mates to simply heave all but the biggest blues over the side in one smooth motion, a majority of private boat anglers prefer lighter tackle and the additional sport it permits. This, in turn, suggests the need for either a larger landing net or a gaff or both.

Whether charter or private, the essential moment comes when the sinker has reached the rod tip and somebody must grab the leader and handline the fish to the boat.

On charterboats this is the mate's job. On private boats it usually falls to a fishing companion to take the leader while the angler moves back with the rod to give the man at the rail plenty of room.

If a private boat is properly equipped, it will have both net and gaff aboard. Once the leader is in the railman's hands the angler can, if he chooses, lay the rod down and assist at the rail. The choice of net, gaff, or swingaboard is made then.

The late Art Perlmutter unhooks an average-size northern New Jersey bluefish aboard a "chum-boat" out of Belmar, New Jersey.

Granting that there are times and fish that require gaffing, the blood spoor usually produced by gaff wounds in coastal waters almost invariably draws attention from sharks. Once aroused by blood scent, sharks have been known to ruin a day's fishing by chopping into hooked, fighting blues before they could be landed. This is especially true when a number of boats are fishing over the same school of blues and numerous gaffs are in use. In one sense it is the same as chumming for sharks.

It is always important for the man handling the leader to wear work gloves to protect his hands against line cuts. Many a seemingly exhausted bluefish has somehow found extra energy when the boat was sighted. The result can be a sudden burst of speed and a bad line burn or cut as the leader zips out between clenched fingers.

Relatively light drag settings are recommended for bluefish trolling, but for reasons other than those cited for headboat chumming.

Trolling rods and lines fished from gunwale-mounted rodholders are the norm among most bluefish anglers. Unlike the angler's arms when he is holding the rod, rodholders do not give when a bluefish strikes.

Because the speed and violence of bluefish in a feeding frenzy is something that must be experienced to be adequately appreciated, many a good rod has been broken off at the butt because of a drag setting just a little bit too tight. Even the best drag mechanisms cannot react fast enough to prevent overload when a big blue blisters in to take the bait.

If during the subsequent fight to land the fish the drag seems too light, then it can be tightened enough to control the run. Rarely if ever is there time to loosen a drag before the line or rod breaks. After each fish is landed, the drag setting should be reset or checked to make sure it is light enough for the next strike.

Surf casting: In many places along the northern coastal range of the bluefish surf casting is the number-one fishing method, based upon the fact that in these places the fish range close inshore and can be reached by such tackle.

During peak bluefish abundance surf casters also take their share of fish along the Carolina coast, the Virginia coast, the Maryland coast (especially off Assateague Island), and many parts of the New Jersey coast.

Lures include most of the "tin squid" type and underwater and surface plugs or spoons. Bait for surf-caught blues includes almost any cut baitfish, such as mullet, menhaden, alewives, and butterfish.

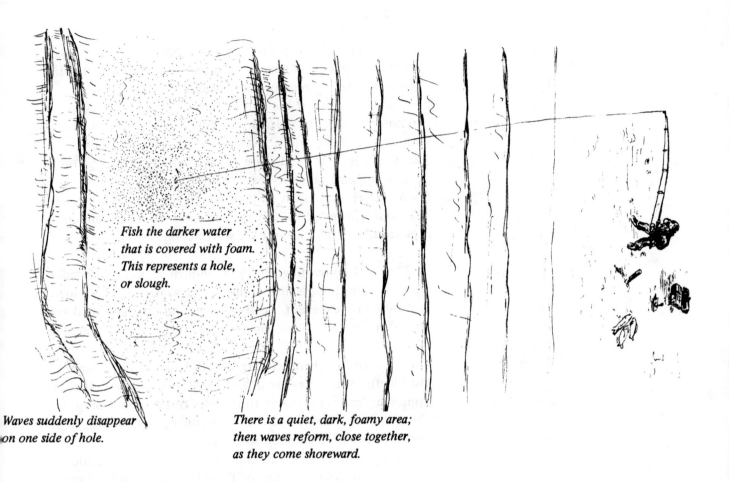

Fish the darker water that is covered with foam. This represents a hole, or slough.

Waves suddenly disappear on one side of hole.

There is a quiet, dark, foamy area; then waves reform, close together, as they come shoreward.

Reading the surf pays off.

Successful surf casting for blues is based mainly on "reading" the surf conditions in any given area. The experienced surf angler reads the bottom contours by observing a wave as it approaches the beach.

Slopes or sloughs (pronounced "slews") run parallel to the beach and are a series of ridges and troughs. Waves passing over the ridges tend to stir the sand in the troughs and expose small bait species. This draws attention from larger baitfish, and the game fish move in to share the feast.

Mullet and numerous other members of the inshore forage species habitually feed in the troughs, and when blues are present within reach of surf-casting gear the action can reach the thrill-a-minute stage.

Generally speaking, surf casters strive to cast their baited hooks or lures beyond the second wave before it begins cresting. It is generally true that a 100-yard cast will produce more

215

action than a 50-yard cast, because blues move into shoal feeding troughs from deeper water. They can be attracted to baits presented even before they reach the troughs.

One way to tell if the bait or lure has reached a trough is to note whether it tends to stay out or seems to be washing ashore. Dropped into a trough, properly weighted baits or lures will tend to hold there as the backwash, or undertow, exerts outgoing pressure near the bottom.

Artificial lures, such as the favored tin squids, which are cast out and reeled in, can be "felt" over the ridges and into the troughs with or against the wave action.

Plug and fly casting: Difficult though it may be to adequately rate the sporting qualities of a game fish whose lowest rating is "excellent," casting plugs and flies into breaking bluefish schools deserves whatever superlative you may apply.

Action that's hard to beat

Not even my cherished largemouth bass can hold a candle to bluefish when they are in a surface-feeding frenzy. At such times anglers can move up to the edge of the school, stop the boat and let it drift, and then cast either plugs, spoons, flies, or all three into the middle of the action.

This is the kind of bluefish sport in which conventional casting rods, spinning gear, or fly-fishing tackle will all score for anglers who use them with even a modest degree of skill.

The most favored way to take advantage of breaking blues is to have casting gear all rigged and ready while trolling. As often happens when blues are abundant, the sight of diving sea gulls perhaps a mile or more away will signal a breaking school. Then is the time to haul in the trolling lines and fire up whatever power you have to get to the scene as quickly as possible. By stopping the engine well before reaching the center of activity, you can let the boat drift in close enough to cast without fear of spooking the fish with engine noises—as unlikely as that may seem.

As sometimes happens, blues will stay on the surface only briefly—until the baitfish are consumed, if it is a small school, or until the onrush of other fishing boats puts them down. And unless you have a private ocean, bay, or river, you can be sure that all other bluefish anglers in sight of the diving gulls will rush to get in on the sport.

216

Bluefish are lady-angler pleasers.
They fight hard enough
to make the distaffers know
they've been fishing and yet
are realistically catchable
on tackle most gals enjoy using.

When the school of blues sounds or moves away as suddenly as it appeared, then it is time to put the trolling lines over the side again and wait for the next sight of diving gulls.

This kind of bluefish sport rarely is available aboard ocean charterboats, mainly because few of them are prepared to fish that way and because breaking fish at sea are a rarity rather than the norm, as they are in rivers and bays. Then, too, the angler who pays charter fees wants to get as much for his money as possible in the way of edible catches. He does not want to spend time waiting for breaking fish.

Fishing for blues will put both the angler and his equipment to the acid test.

BLUEFISH TACKLE

The phrase "terminal tackle" means whatever is attached to the end of the fishing line, regardless of what kind of line it is or what kind of fish are being sought. In saltwater fishing generally, and in bluefishing especially, the security of the terminal tackle is primary because the fight of a hooked bluefish will strain to the utmost every knot, snap, or swivel used.

Recommended knots attaching terminal rigs, shown in the section "Fishing Tips and Techniques," should be tied carefully and drawn tight to avoid slippage or loss of line strength because of improperly tied knots.

All monofilament line, regardless of size or test strength, is inclined to be slippery when tied. The larger the line diameter and test strength, the more apt it is to slip at the knots unless one (or more) of the recommended knots is used. Test all knots with a strong, sustained pull by hand before using them.

All hardware (snaps and snap swivels) used for bluefishing should be rated to stand at least twice as much pull as the rated strength of the line being used.

In the realm of adequate rods and reels to take bluefish, it is wiser by far to err on the heavy side than on the light side. Few reels designed primarily for use on freshwater species of fish will stand up to the beating they can and probably will get from bluefishing.

218

Aboard a bluefish "chum-boat"
off the Jersey Coast. Heavy tackle
is prescribed for this kind
of sport to prevent as many
line tangles as possible.

In the early days of spinning, shortly after World War II, a friend of mine was determined to take blues on his newly acquired freshwater spinning outfit, one of the best of its time. Less than two hours after we left the fishing docks at Ocean City, Maryland, he had completely ruined three new spinning reels on less than a dozen bluefish.

The sustained pull of a fighting blue will stretch any line, thereby reducing its diameter while it is under strain. When the fight is over and all the line is back on the reel, the line will begin to regain its lost diameter, applying enormous side pressure on the ends of any reel spool used.

Two of my friend's spinning reels simply exploded from just such internal line pressure. The third stripped its gears during the fight with—and loss of—a bluefish that looked as if it weighed not more than five or six pounds. That was before the advent of saltwater spinning reels built to stand the strain.

By any standards, anyplace, the bluefish is a superb antagonist when hooked on tackle with heft enough to do the job. Anything less is foolish showmanship, not sportsmanship.

Working sea gulls, a sure sign blues are chasing and chopping baitfish.

221

Chapter eighteen

The Florida Keys

Of all fishing opportunities available in North America, only the famed Florida Keys can be validly described as having no equal in terms of variety, abundance, and easy accessibility. If I had to give an unqualified recommendation about where a fisherman can get "the mostest for the leastest," the Keys would win hands down.

From Miami southward the Keys are a series of small islands, most of which are connected by a causeway that extends nearly 180 miles from end to end. With rare exceptions, every mile is fishable. From Key Biscayne, the northernmost of the group, to Key West, at the end of the chain, there are literally hundreds of fishing centers and guides ranging in reputation from famous to relatively new in the business. And even the newcomers to the guiding profession in the Keys are, in a word, good, most of them having been brought up in the area by the older hands.

More important for those who may be traveling long distances burdened by a shortage of time, in my experience there has been no such thing as a blank day, or "You should have been here last week."

For many years it was my good fortune to visit the Keys beginning about December 10 and extending to what my wife labeled "dangerously close to Christmas Eve." Each year just before I boarded the plane to Miami I got the same wifely admonition—"If you don't get back in time for Christmas, don't bother to come back."

She was joking, of course. At least I like to think she was, but there was an element of sincerity in the warning.

I confess that the temptation to stay and fish just one or two more days arose numerous times. With equal candor, I'm not really sure whether the main drawback was my wife's warning or my depleted checking account. Nor am I alone in that semivice.

A fishing crony to whom I recounted tales of the Keys saved his money for two years until he had enough to see him through a week, hitting only the highlights. Promising his bride of less than a year that he would grace her table again, without fail, one week from the date of departure, he actually got back home 32 days later. Yes, he is still married to the same girl.

My own exposure to fishing the Keys was as close to idyllic as fishing can get.

One of my oldest and best friends is the world-famed angling expert, Lefty Kreh. At the time of my first visit Lefty was the director of the Metropolitan Miami Fishing Tournament, one of the biggest and oldest of its kind anyplace. He selected early December because only then could he devote a week to guiding me in the Keys. Warning me that fishing in December "is not much to crow about," Lefty then proceeded to show me more varieties and abundance of fishing than I had seen in all the rest of my life put together. (December was good for another reason. It is off season, and the prices are lower for just about everything on which you have to spend money.)

When Lefty picked me up at the Miami airport on my first trip to his region, he asked me what kind of fishing I'd like to try. In my virginal ignorance, I asked what he had to offer. It took him the best part of 30 minutes to run down the list of species, places, and methods. "Later on," he added, "fishing gets real good here, usually beginning about March."

I opted, first, for having a go at light tackle tarpon fishing, adding that with my lack of experience I did not want to get tangled up with fish in the hundred-pound range. With a grin that reminded me of what a weasel might look like after he had just raided a henhouse, Lefty agreed to do his best to arrange something to my liking.

Early the next morning we were cutting a silver wake on the fringe waters of the Everglades in Lefty's 20-foot fiberglass fishing boat, doing about 35 knots. After about 45 minutes of high-speed travel, he cut the power and headed straight for what looked to me like a solid wall of mangroves. When we got to the edge of the tangled mass, Lefty instructed me to "hunker down in the bow of the boat and reach overhead to help pull us through the mangrove thicket."

After about ten minutes of literally forcing the boat through the tangle, we emerged into a small canal. By my arithmetic we were about 27 miles into the wilds of the Everglades. But my eyes told me we were several million years into the past. Primeval is the only word to describe the unique sights and sounds, the utter "otherworldliness" of the scene.

Being a sensitive man, Lefty had anticipated my awestruck reaction. He was prepared for a moment or two of silence while I tried to absorb the wonders of this hidden, otherwise inaccessible natural canal.

Finally he interrupted my reverie with: "Hey Yankee, if you've finished gawking for a while we'll get on to where the tarpon are waiting."

224

Bluefish

The battling, biting, bloodthirsty bluefish is an opponent worthy of all the strength and skill an angler has at his command.

The blue isn't a large fish, but it will tax your fishing ability. With its lightning-fast strike and powerful determination to avoid being caught, you'll know you've been in a fight by the time you boat one.

In the northern part of the bluefish's range, surf casting is one of the most popular methods of fishing for blues. And from Cape Cod to the Carolinas, when blues are abundant, anglers trot out their surf-casting gear to storm the beaches for blues.

Plug or fly casting into a school of blues in a feeding frenzy will take many fish. In the throes of one of these frenzies, the fish will take anything that's offered to them.

Chumming and trolling are favored bluefishing methods, too. A keen sense of smell makes the bluefish a natural for chumming. Blues prefer oily fish—butterfish, menhaden—but when they're hungry, which is almost always, any offering will be eagerly accepted.

Bluefishing time is one time when any angler—young or old, male or female—is ready, willing, and eager to "get the blues."

*"Baby" tarpon abound
in the canals
of the Keys.*

With that he fired up the outboard again and we streaked along that narrow canal at the same 35 knots employed on open water. I couldn't help wondering what would happen if we hit a cypress stump or something and sheared the proppin. You can't row a 20-foot boat even if you have oars, which we didn't.

About five minutes later Lefty cut the engine and picked up his pushpole to ease us along the canal silently.

Pointing to a mass of small bubbles on the water ahead, Lefty said: "Okay, they're here." He later explained that tarpon leave such bubble evidence when they move into calm waters to feed.

As we moved along, making scarcely a ripple, Lefty predicted we'd see tarpon rolling just around the next bend where the canal widened to become a small pondlike area. Despite his detailed description of what we would find around that bend, I was not prepared for the sight that met us.

He had placed me in the bow, a choice casting position, with my medium-action spinning rod and a jointed plug all ready to cast at the first fish I saw.

I didn't see a fish. I saw several dozen fish, all rolling their silvery dorsals and backs out of the water like a school of porpoises. I stood there, rigid with indecision. Which way should I cast first?

When I turned around, mouth agape, Lefty said: "It's your move, pal. You can stand there and just admire them or you can unfreeze your arm and toss that plug. But make up your mind before they decide to leave."

I came to enough to drop the big jointed Bassmaster about a hundred feet out. I saw at least six fish charge the plug.

My first battle with what Lefty scathingly had labeled "those damn little tarpon" (20- to 30-pounders) lasted all of two or three seconds before the leaping, headshaking slab of silver fury tossed that plug and its oversize treble hooks back in my face. And I mean that literally. That hook-adorned fishgrabber whistled maliciously past my head, and to this day I don't understand how it missed.

Then Lefty told me the trick to fighting a tarpon is to give slack by lowering the rod tip instantly when the fish jumps. "If you don't," he warned, "you just might wind up with that plug in your own mouth."

Time after time that day I had tarpon strike my plug and knock it out of the water, or hit and get hooked momentarily only to throw the plug with the first spectacular leap and have a second tarpon take the plug when it landed again in the water.

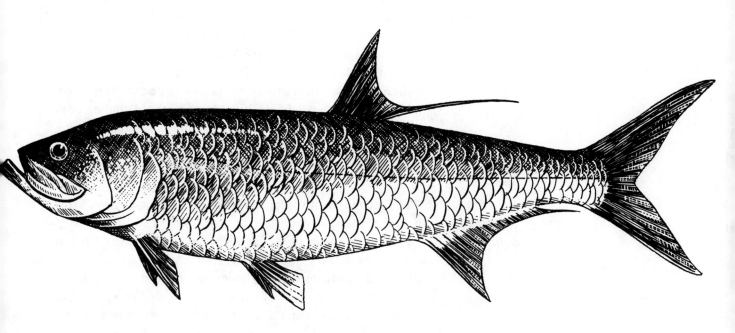

TARPON

Megalops atlantica

World record
283 pounds

Taken in
Lake Maracaibo, Venezuela
March 1956

I had heard tales of such action, and more, from my father, including accounts of tarpon leaping into the boat with the fishermen. Exaggerated as I thought most such stories, none matched the real thing I experienced that day deep in the "you-can't-get-out-from-here" wilderness of the Everglades with Lefty Kreh. For that trip alone—not counting the years before and after—I owe my buddy a debt I'll never be able to repay.

Experts such as Lefty Kreh, Stu Apt, the late Joe Brooks, and a few others set their light-tackle sights for tarpon in the hundred-pound range. And by "light tackle" I mean saltwater fly rods equipped with leader tippets testing not more than 10 pounds for official record catches.

Granted, they do not wrestle such monsters in the confines of an Everglades canal or bay but stick to open water where a fish can jump and fight itself to death without finding anything to snag the leader on. Still, landing a tarpon weighing a hundred pounds or more on a fly rod, no matter where, when, or how, is a feat of gargantuan proportions.

Bonefish—
"greased
lightning"

The second most spectacular fish on my Florida Keys list is the bonefish.

To "break me in right," as Lefty put it, he booked me to fish with bonefish guide Bill Curtis, of Key Biscayne.

Bill is a full-fledged, 12-cylinder character in his own right. In demand to the point of often being booked at least a year ahead, Bill believes that anyone who really wants to go bonefishing with him has an obligation to get to his dock at the appointed time. (And that doesn't mean five minutes late, or you'll likely see him and his boat on their way to the bonefish flats without you.)

As is always true of the best in Florida Keys fishing, a good guide is essential, at least the first time. Bonefishing is unique, however, in that a good guide *remains* essential unless you can stay long enough to learn to read the local tides, weather conditions, and phases of the moon—and *then* be able to correlate those factors with some seat-of-the-pants luck. You just might come up with a fish or two by yourself.

Bonefish do not jump. In fact, the most spectacular thing about the bonefish is not the fight it puts up but that first, totally unbelievable run.

228

*Bonefish, the wariest
of them all.*

Many fly-rod experts take bonefish on streamers, or what Ted Williams calls his special "shrimp fly." For the average visitor the best lure is live shrimp fished with medium-action spinning tackle equipped with at least 200 yeards of not less than 8-pound-test monofilament line. (Even with 200 yards of brand new "string" aboard the reel, it is a wise angler who has another 400 yards in the spare-parts locker.) Here, too, is the place and the fish that will test the capabilities of your spinning-reel drag mechanism.

Bonefish guides usually stand in the back of the boat watching for fish as they pole the boat over the flats in shallow, gin-clear water. When they see a fish, they tell the angler where to cast his whole live shrimp so it lands ahead of the moving fish and sinks to the bottom naturally. If the fish takes the bait you set the hook—*hard*—then instantly lift the rod as high over your head as you can reach and just hold on and hope.

Setting the hook in a bonefish is akin to pulling the trigger on a high-powered rifle with your line tied to the bullet. Regardless of previous fishing experience, nothing that went before is adequate to prepare you for that first bonefish run, in terms of both length and speed.

Why the need for 200 yards of line? Believe it or not, a big bone is more likely than not to take almost that much in one water-scorching run. You hold the rod tip as high as possible to keep all that line from getting nicked or sliced off by sharp coral.

I've got to admit that once you stop the initial run—if and when you stop it, that is—the rest of the fight is more like a throbbing tug-of-war with your adversary having all the advantages. Lest I get a letter-bomb in the next mail from Bill Curtis, let me hasten to add that the "throbbing tug-of-war" described above is not meant to belittle the fish or its fight except by comparison with that first run. Exaggerated? Tell me about it after your first bonefish.

*Frenzy
with fins*

The next Florida Keys offering on my list is the jack crevalle. If you are a saltwater fan who has messed around with any of the really strong oceanic fish, you will instantly recognize the jack crevalle for what it is the first time you get a side view of one.

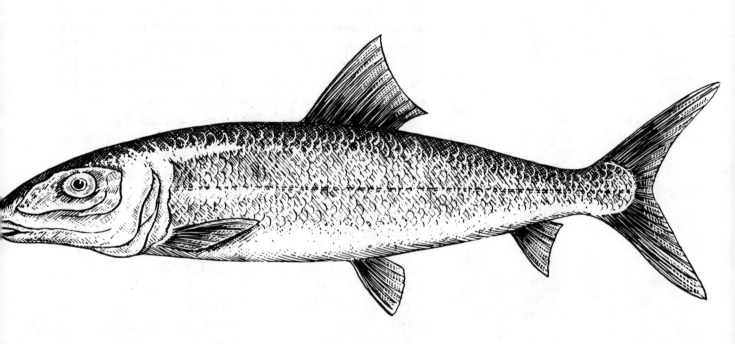

BONEFISH

Albula vulpes

World record
19 pounds
Taken in
Zululand, South Africa
May 1962

After landing the first one, no matter how small it may be, grab it across the back and squeeze. It's like trying to squeeze a hockey puck—just plain muscle, and a heap of it. No place is that fact better demonstrated than on the end of a line.

My initiation into the loyal order of jack crevalle catchers occurred while Lefty and I were anchored between two small islands off Key West waiting for, as he put it, "the tide to bring tarpon through the cut." While we were waiting I tied on my favorite tarpon plug, that same jointed Bassmaster mentioned above, and began casting to pass the time.

Suddenly the rod was jerked almost out of my hand. I've read such claims many times, but before that afternoon I always had disbelieved them—such things just don't happen.

When I yelled, a weakness of mine each time I get a strike of any kind, including bluegills, Lefty smiled and said, "Nope, it's not a tarpon, but wait until you see what size it is."

About 20 minutes later I finally got a little 4-pound jack crevalle close enough to be netted.

We had a real, 15-round championship bout with jack crevalles on a later trip out of Key West. Doc Jacobson was with me on that trip to what we called "Lefty's Land." We were fishing near a sunken destroyer the U.S. Navy had once used as a target.

The old hulk was more out of the water than in it, and a school of jacks had herded a jillion sardines up against the side of the ship. The jacks were cutting through the baitfish like a herd of vacuum cleaners, and we were hooking and landing them as fast as any man can land 20-pound-and-over jacks—which isn't very fast. It took all that our heavy-action spinning rods could muster in the way of backbone to handle those raging jacks after they took our Mylar jigs.

That day was my last session with jack crevalles, but I figure I had at least five years' worth of jack experience on that one trip. Doc, who had caught almost every game fish there is except jack crevalle, talked in his sleep about them half the night.

Barracuda territory

Earlier that same day Lefty had taken us about 15 miles off Key West to a circle of mangroves called the Marquesas to fish for barracuda while waiting for the tide to bring the jack crevalles into action.

232

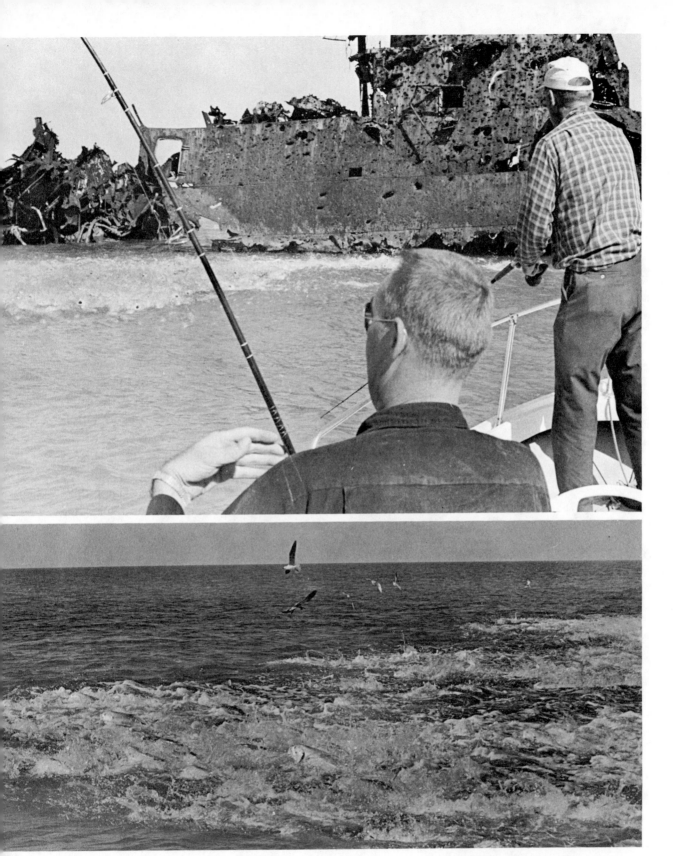

*Schools of jack crevalles
churn the water into froth
during a feeding frenzy.*

Once inside the circle you are in 'cuda territory with a vengeance. We had taken barracuda before, some in the 25-pound range, and I had caught bigger ones than that off Bermuda several years before. I thought I was fairly well schooled in handling them. But when they charge a topwater plug in squads it gets a little unnerving, especially when all you can see are fish in the 30- to 40-pound weight bracket.

Seeing the fish as they strike is one of the fascinating bonuses one gets when fishing in most Florida offshore waters. And off Key West the water is so clear that with certain light conditions it simply disappears, visually.

Most Keys fishing centers offer deep-sea fishing charterboat services. We tried that, just to say we had not missed anything. By preference, however, I'll take the shallow water, small-boat fishing, such as Lefty showed me so many unforgettable times.

The list of spectacular fish to be caught in the Florida Keys is legion. Because I restricted my own trips to December, I missed out on some of the species. By the same token, I don't know what I'd have done with anything more on my angling plate than I had.

It is a lost cause to attempt to really describe Florida Keys fishing in one chapter. I am convinced it would take several books to do it justice.

Ladyfish, snook, redfish, permit, and a crockful of lesser species are all available among the inshore waters in and around the Keys. There is almost no place along the Keys Causeway where a traveling angler can't stop and catch fish of some kind right from shore. Night fishing for big tarpon in the canal that adjoins the highway is a thrill that should not be missed. And by all means, try a deep-sea trip for giant groupers—and a lot of other fish that you will get in the bargain.

Most important of all, even if you have to save up for 10 years just for one week in the Keys, do it. You will never regret it. Neither will you ever forget it.

*Lefty Kreh, holder of numerous
world records in the saltwater
fly-fishing league, gaffs
a barracuda, the biggest
he ever landed on any tackle.*

LEFTY KREH'S FLORIDA KEYS FISHING TIMETABLE

As might have been concluded from statements included in the foregoing text of this chapter, I hold my old friend and fishing companion, Lefty Kreh, in high esteem. He is both a man of exceptional principles and an expert on fishing in the Florida Keys.

Unlike most of us in the fishing fraternity, Lefty's use of adjectives and superlatives to describe fishing in the Keys is amazingly accurate, even though he admits to an abounding enthusiasm for the area himself. Therefore, in his own words, the following is Lefty's Florida Keys Fishing Timetable:

January and February: The Key West area is red hot at this time of year. Out where the waters of the Gulf of Mexico mix with those of the Atlantic Ocean a migration of baitfish congregate during January and February. These include ballyhoo, pilchards, alewives, and sardines.

Key West Harbor is alive with tarpon that hang around the heated waters coming from the local power plant.

The reef line that runs from Key West toward the Marquesas and the Tortugas is loaded with barracudas and mackerel, king mackerel (called kingfish there) are found along the drop-offs, and sailfish are still around. Amberjacks can be taken on the wrecks along the reef line.

Large schools of jack crevalle roam the coral upcroppings between the Marquesas and Smith Shoal in the Gulf of Mexico west and northwest of Key West.

Smith Shoal can be stacked up with king mackerel, jack crevalle, and cobia. Smith Shoal is located about 14 miles northwest of Key West and can be approached through the Calda Channel running through the shallows to within 7 miles of the shoal itself.

In many areas of the Keys highway, bridge fishing is good at night. At such times and places snapper, grouper, and some tarpon are to be found under bridges such as Tom's Harbor Cut, Indian Key Bridge, Long Key Viaduct Bridge, and Seven Mile Bridge.

A delicate touch on the fly rod is what it takes to land a tarpon on a streamer fly.

Bonefishing at this time of the year is spotty, as is permit fishing. Cold fronts and high winds too often spoil this kind of fishing during January and February.

When cold winds do not blow, what is known as the "backcountry area" between Islamorada, Jewfish Creek, and the mainland where the Everglades lie, can be good for snook, sea trout, and redfish.

Toward the last of February the first of the giant tarpon can be expected to begin migrating from the ocean depths toward Key West, appearing first in Pearl Basin, Northwest Channel, and in the harbor itself. One of the world's record tarpon taken on a fly rod was caught there during late February.

Late February also marks the appearance of cobia in large numbers in the Gulf of Mexico, off Smith Shoal, and around the buoys in the harbor.

March: Tarpon are all but certain to be massing to move into the lower Keys and the Key West area. Bonefishing will begin to improve as the cold fronts become less frequent and less severe for this area. It should be remembered, however, that March winds can cancel any fishing trip aimed at the shallow bonefish flats.

Snook should begin to show up in Florida Bay. Guides from Tavernier Key down to Marathon can be expected to produce results.

Florida Bay fishing will begin to approach the excellent mark, with bluefish, ladyfish, and mackerel on the fishing menu. The region behind Long Key to Sugar Loaf Key is best.

Bridge fishing in the Keys will be greatly improved by now.

April: This month marks the beginning of the giant tarpon run in Florida Bay from Key West past Islamorada. This is perhaps the most exciting of all light-tackle fishing in the Keys. Literally hundreds of tarpon swarm into this area from the deeps offshore. Some think they come in to spawn.

Bonefishing is on the upswing; also, a few permit will be available on the same bonefish flats.

Snook will begin to move into the backcountry and along the coastal sloughs and rivers of the Everglades.

A giant tarpon takes to the air.

May: Most light-tackle anglers who know the Keys prefer May. The weather usually is good, and huge tarpon are at a peak of abundance in the backcountry. Bonefish feed on the flats all day when the tide is high enough in lower Biscayne Bay and in the Islamorada-Marathon area.

Snook migrate in huge numbers at this time of the year, ranging up the West Coast of Florida and the coastal areas along the Everglades.

Redfish and sea trout are plentiful on the flats of Florida Bay.

Bridge fishing is at a peak this time of the year. The best times are after dark. Then, you can stop at most any of the Keys bridges and listen to big tarpon rolling before casting a bait to them.

June: This is number two on the light-tackle angler's hit parade of fishing times. Giant tarpon now move to the ocean side of the Keys from their stay in Florida Bay.

Bonefishing still is good, but the midday heat can be uncomfortable. Best times are early morning and late afternoon. This will last through September.

Permit disappear from the flats in June, but they can be found in huge numbers around all the wrecks.

June is the time when redfish are at their peak in Florida Bay. They seem to like the warm shallows.

July: By now the big tarpon are gone, except for a few that seem to linger here all year.

Bonefishing remains good early and late, and permit will be on the flats in water depths from 18 to 24 inches. Crabs are the best bait for permit.

August: This is a slow month for most fishing, except for redfish, which continue to feed heavily in the warm waters of the flats.

September: This month is a repeat of August.

October: This is the third month in preference among light-tackle anglers. Baby tarpon move in, redfishing remains good,

*Not all of the Keys' tarpon
are taken on light tackle.*

along with snook. Ocean fishing begins in earnest, and bone-fishing on the flats picks up.

November: This month is a repeat of October.

December: The northern fishes that shun the cold—cobia, mackerel, king mackerel, and tuna—are available in huge numbers now. This is followed by a real run of jack crevalles until sometime in March when all leave for parts unknown.

December is the peak month for sailfish from Islamorada to Key West.

King mackerel, cobia, bonito, and amberjacks move into the Smith Shoal area of Key West. Though redfish will be scarce now, spotted sea trout often are abundant.

*Fighting a fish of this size
on a fly rod can take hours.
Most tarpon are released.*

243

Chapter nineteen

Big-game fishing

Big-game fishing is a highly specialized form of angling that many fishermen think about, some even dream about, but relatively few ever experience.

In part, at least, the lack of widespread participation in big-game fishing is due to the costs involved and the need for expert guidance.

Big-game fishing tackle, for example, is astonishingly expensive and is of no use whatever for any other kind of fishing. Similarly, offshore fishing cruisers usually are in the 40-foot class for length, are powered by twin engines capable of 20 knots or more, and have hulls built to stand up to the punishment that the sea can give any boat caught in even a mild blow.

WHITE MARLIN
Tetrapturus albidus

World record
159 pounds, 8 ounces

Taken in
Pompano Beach, Florida
April 1953

*Even though it doesn't challenge
the record, this white marlin
would make any angler proud
of his catch.*

When you add to those factors the cost of fuel and maintenance and then drop in a suitable profit for the captain and mate plus a fair return on what is a big investment in boats and equipment, the daily charter fees needed to cover all such items can seem huge.

Lest I be chained to a sinking 40-foot offshore big-game cruiser, let me hasten to admit that there are some sports who own boats rigged mainly for offshore big-game fish that are not anywhere near 40 feet long.

Wherever billfish and others in the big-game category range close enough to shore for an easy run-in to beat impending bad weather, you are likely to find examples of what I call "mini-marlin-boats," complete with outriggers and fighting chairs. The ones I have seen have ranged from about 20 to 25 feet in length. Most are made of fiberglass to withstand the pounding that can take place with hasty beats for the docks.

To offset those admittedly discouraging figures, there is no denying the unparalleled thrill of hooking and fighting almost any of the species listed among big-game fish.

My first white marlin crashed the baits during my first trip offshore many years ago. In sharp contrast to that good fortune, I know one marlin-fishing addict who spent more than $20,000 in charter fees and other expenses before he landed his first marlin.

Except in rare instances (and none that I can actually cite), charter fees cover the cost of the captain (expert guide), the mate, and use of the tackle.

The treatment and services usually include rigging all rods, reels, and lines with whatever is required for the fish being sought. This is the mate's job, and it is done more to assure proper rigging than to impress the anglers aboard.

Depending upon the individual's personal desires, the mate will actually hook a client's first fish for him, then hand him the rod after the client is firmly established in the fighting chair. From that point on, it is likely that both the captain and the mate will offer rapid-fire advice to the novice angler while he fights the fish.

In fact, most captains and mates find it hard to resist offering advice even to experienced anglers. They, too, love the sport. But a more practical reason for their advice is that their reputation hangs on how many fish are brought to the docks

The last leap...

or how many "release flags" are flying when you return at the end of the day. Their reputation is not enhanced by how thrilled the novice angler was just before he lost his first fish.

Albeit the captain's motives may be at least semiself-serving, both he and the mate will be doing all they can to assure a successful trip.

In some well known big-game fishing areas—Mazatlan, Mexico, for one—some charter captains have been known to guarantee fish to the client. No fish, no fee.

I suspect that the words on this page will outlive that particular practice as costs continue to rise. But for as long as it lasts, and in the places where it exists, the first-timer can take advantage of it.

For those who have never been offshore before, it is wise to assume that seasickness is at least a possibility. To prevent ruining what could be considered a once-in-a-lifetime outlay of cash for big-game fishing, be sure to get a supply of doctor-recommended antiseasickness pills and take them as directed. Some compounds induce sleepiness, others have different side effects; but regardless of the secondary reaction that may or may not intrude, none will be as totally devastating as the seasickness itself.

Except for those fortunate persons for whom money is no object and big-game fishing is a regular event, few fishermen manage to amass any significant expertise in the subject because opportunities for practical application are not that plentiful.

To complicate the learning process even more, advice given by one charter captain may—and likely will—conflict in some ways with that given by another captain.

I remember being lectured for most of an hour on how white marlin strike the baits being trolled for them. "White marlin," said my mentor of the moment, "always move into the baits in plain sight [the baits are trolled skipping over the surface of the water], then hit the bait they choose with their bills to kill it.

"Then," he continued, "they come back to pick it up and swallow it."

He went on to tell me that as soon as the marlin "bills the bait," as it is called by some, the angler is supposed to put the reel in free-spool, allowing the line to run out and leaving the

*Billfishing with a fly rod
is a game for the practiced artisan.*

bait motionless in the water as though it had been killed. "They don't just rush up and grab the bait like those bass you've been catching," he added.

Fish,
like people,
are individuals

About the only point he forgot was to invite my first marlin to his lecture. Not being aware that marlin "don't just rush up and grab the bait," mine did just that: grabbed it and hooked itself before anybody on board knew it was in the same ocean with us.

My next four white marlin, on subsequent trips, also were unaware of that captain's considered opinion because each did the same thing. Then, finally, I found a conformist.

In the meantime, though, I had had expert information from a number of different charter captains, and no two stories were alike.

There are a number of "tricks" that work on some marlin. There are none that work on all marlin. For example, if a marlin shows up cruising among the trolled baits but refuses to take, one recommended procedure is to grab the rod out of the holder and begin reeling the bait in fast. This is supposed to make the fish think its quarry is getting away and will, reputedly, evoke a solid strike. Sometimes it even works.

On one trip when I was running a camera, one of the clients in the cockpit tossed a shiny beercan overboard after emptying it. The can bobbed and tossed in the wash of the boat for about 20 feet when a marlin streaked in and hit it a can-crushing wallop with its bill, ignoring four real baits all around it.

Having been duped by a phony, that particular marlin departed. Less than five minutes later a marlin at least two feet longer than the beercan-sucker bored in past the four baits and hit the teaser, which is trolled on a short line tied to the center of the stern and is hookless.

I have talked for a total of hours to other marlin fishermen, and according to some accounts, marlin do indeed act like they are supposed to. But from my own experience, and that of numerous others, the only thing about marlin fishing that is remotely predictable is its unpredictability.

It is important to the novice big-game fisherman to avoid any feeling of inferiority if the first—or even the second and third—big fish gets away. Even the really expert tournament

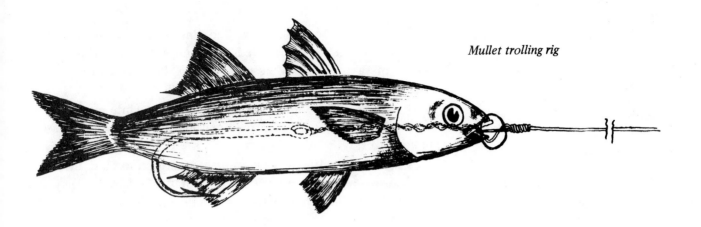

Mullet trolling rig

*Thrust a crochet hook
through the abdominal cavity of the mullet
and out through its mouth.
Hook a loop of leader wire
and pull the loop back through the fish.*

*Open the eye of the fish hook slightly,
slip the loop of leader into the hook eye,
then close the eye with pliers.*

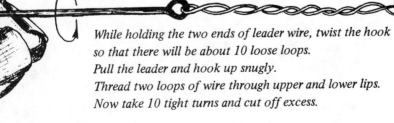

*While holding the two ends of leader wire, twist the hook
so that there will be about 10 loose loops.
Pull the leader and hook up snugly.
Thread two loops of wire through upper and lower lips.
Now take 10 tight turns and cut off excess.*

anglers lose fish now and then, and I'm talking about men who have spent many hundreds of hours big-game fishing. Matter of fact, if they were easy to land, they wouldn't be classed as big-game fish.

Among the species listed as big-game fish are white marlin, blue marlin, black marlin, striped marlin, sailfish, swordfish, mako sharks, wahoos, and giant tuna.

Of that list, white marlin, sailfish, and wahoos are the smallest in terms of average size. But what they lack in size compared to others on the list is more than made up in sheer uninhibited action when hooked.

This is not to say the larger fish do not give a good accounting of themselves. Neither do I mean to imply that the bigger fish do not jump—though some do not. But it is like watching a lightweight boxing match on one hand and a heavyweight wrestling match on the other hand.

Although there are many fishermen who would probably disagree, as a matter of personal preference I would without reservation choose white marlin and wahoos over all other species for the best in fishing sport.

The first wahoo I hooked, I fought for at least 30 minutes and finally lost the battle when it elected to run under the boat and cut the line on the propellers.

I was fishing out of Ocean City, Maryland, with Captain Reese Layton, one of the best big-game skippers and a man who, when he wasn't chartering, was out there fishing for the sport of it.

I had served many times as mate for Reese and many more times as one of a two-man team who just went offshore to see what we could find.

The day in question was ideal for white marlin. We had seen nearly a dozen just "tailing" along on the surface with their dorsals showing. But we somehow couldn't evoke a strike.

Wahoo!
A fish that
deserves its name

About midday, when the ocean had flattened out like a pool table, which is considered bad for fishing, we were somewhat less than wide awake when suddenly about 6½ feet of wahoo exploded out of the ocean about a hundred yards away. The fish had leaped in the course of either chasing bait or being chased by something bigger than it was.

252

*Marlin are among the gamiest
of the big-game species.*

Reese swung the helm and we turned to troll over the area where the wahoo had jumped. In mere minutes I was hooked up to what felt like a P-38 fighter in a power dive. Then the fish leaped clear of the surface, not once but time after time.

At one point in the fight I had less than 20 turns of line left on the reel. Several times Reese swung the boat fast and ran down on the fish to let me regain more line.

When the fight was nearly over, the fish took a sudden dashing turn right for the boat, and that ended the battle.

Disappointed? Sorry? Not really. I had had the fun of fighting the fish and would have released it had I won the battle. My arms and shoulders felt like they were made of wet dishrags. Until you try fighting a big-game fish, don't scoff at that comparison.

I have seen otherwise husky young men in the prime of physical condition actually give up during prolonged fights with big white marlin in the 60- to 70-pound weight range. This is a good way to lose a marlin, and more times than not they did just that as soon as they tried to rest by holding the rod tip high without pumping and reeling, keeping the pressure on the fish.

The first big tuna is apt to be a muscle-wrenching experience somewhat akin to lifting a 10-gallon oil drum full of wet sand several hundred feet while it is hanging on the end of a fishing rod.

Tuna fight deep. The bigger the fish the deeper it will sound when hooked. Then, when it has gone down as far as it wants to—and *that* you cannot stop—the slugfest will begin. I have never caught a really giant tuna—one in the 400- or 500-pound range—but the 155-pounder I did land made me wince in sheer pain each time it shook its head during the fight.

When it was over, more than two hours after the strike, my arms hung like limp noodles on either side of the chair. I didn't have the strength to lift them for several minutes.

I cannot claim that there is anything really spectacular about the fight of a big tuna. It is more a contest of grunt and muscle; a wrestling match. Neither is the mako shark as prone to leaping as any of the marlins or the wahoo. But both should be experienced at least one time. The least it will do is make you appreciate the fighting ability of the billfishes, which is what the marlin, sailfish, and swordfish are called.

There is an abundance of big-game fishing along both coasts of North America as well as in the Gulf of Mexico.

Wherever coastal resort areas are established, you are more than likely to find ample big-game fishing charter fleets ready to serve you.

As with most commercial endeavors, there are charter captains who are excellent and charter captains who will cheerfully give you nothing more than a boat ride for your fees and charter captains who cover the whole range in between those extremes. Fortunately, the good ones are the norm.

To take a fling at this admittedly exotic form of angling experience, all you need do is visit the nearest offshore fishing dock and arrange for a trip. You don't have to bring anything with you except money. All tackle and other needed equipment is furnished in most places for the charter fees.

Big-game fishing is always available

Chapter twenty

Fishing tips and techniques

The material in this chapter will, hopefully, give you some tips and introduce you to some techniques that will improve your fishing performance and add to your enjoyment.

You may find that some of the tips offered here can save you a lot of aggravation and—if they relate to care of equipment—a lot of expense. They could save a lot of fish, too, that might otherwise have been numbered among the ones that got away.

These tips and techniques are based on my own experiences—some good, some bitter—and on the experiences of my fishing friends. I've included them in this book to help other fishermen avoid some of the pitfalls that await unwary anglers.

256

Freshwater tackle maintenance: The surest "maintenance therapy" that can be given to any and all freshwater fishing tackle is thorough washing with fresh water after each trip.

This applies especially to trips where slightly salty water is encountered. Known among fishermen as "brackish" water, there usually is enough salt content to quickly ruin many freshwater reels and rod-guides unless the salt is thoroughly flushed off with fresh water immediately after fishing. The next morning could be too late.

Surf-casting reels are subject to having blowing particles of sand lodge in places where they can cause damage. Here, too, a thorough flushing with fresh water will help keep the sand washed out.

Though there are dozens of fishing-reel lubricants on the market, I have found from a few bitter experiences that the most dependable are those containing silicone. The best emergency lube to carry in the tackle box is ordinary petroleum jelly.

Drag setting: All fishing reels equipped with drags (slip-clutches) are subject to failure at critical times unless drag mechanisms are properly cared for.

Proper care for most such reels means simply keeping them clean and free of sand or salt particles.

Some mechanisms contain a series of friction washers sandwiched between bronze or brass slip-washers. Drag adjustment is obtained by screw pressure against these stacks of washers. If grit or corrosion gets into such stacks it can make the drag stick just when it should give line freely—when you are fighting a big fish.

When adjusting a drag setting to suit whatever line is on the reel, it is vital to thread the line through the rod-guides first.

By tying the end of the line on some solid object and setting the drag adjustment to slip before the line breaks, you can assure yourself that the friction between the line and the guides will be accounted for in the drag setting.

TACKLE

Drag settings should be tested after tying the line by reeling in all slack and then lifting the rod tip sharply to impose a sudden, intense strain on the whole rig. If the line doesn't slip when the rod is bent significantly, you had better loosen the drag setting until it does.

Under the strain of a sustained long run, such as in bonefishing, drag mechanisms, even the best of them, tend to heat up and expand. This gives the same effect as tightening the drag.

A drag setting that is a little too loose can be corrected while the fish is running. Rarely can an angler react quickly enough to decrease a too-tight drag setting before the fish breaks his line.

Anglers who for any reason do not wish to or cannot take their own reels apart for at least annual inspection and maintenance should have it done by reel-repair services offered by many fishing tackle stores.

Buying monofilament line: Most monofilament fishing line used today is produced by either the same manufacturer or by the same manufacturing process licensed by the developer. DuPont is outstanding in this field.

Though there is some traffic in what might be called "reprocessing" of second-rate monofilament, no brand-name line I know of is on that list of reprocessed lines.

Some monofilament is put through additional and often secret processes after the prime manufacturer makes it. This results in superior strength for a given line diameter, superior pliability, or nick resistance.

It doesn't always follow that the most expensive lines are the best but as a rule of thumb, that is the safest course to take. The fishing-tackle industry today is one of the most highly competitive we have. No manufacturer is going to chance financial disaster by pricing itself out of the market.

When buying monofilament, look for a tackle shop that offers to fill your reel spools from bulk spools of name-brand line. Usually such shops sell their line by the yard, filling each spool to its proper level and with consistent line tension.

Monofilament lines in the 2-pound to 4-pound test range are best restricted to use with what is known as "ultralight" tackle—those fairy wand rods and miniature reels once so

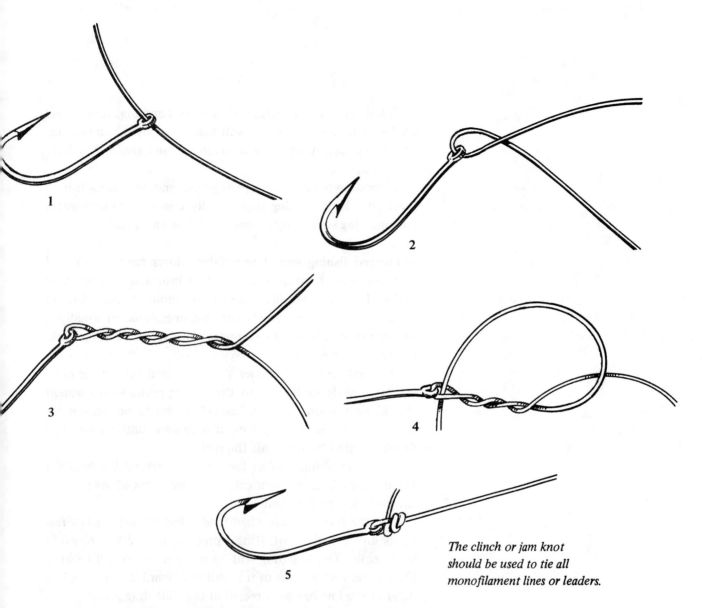

1

2

3

4

5

*The clinch or jam knot
should be used to tie all
monofilament lines or leaders.*

popular for a wide range of fishing, but which in recent years
have proved inadequate for most fishing.

For my freshwater spinning and plug casting, the lightest
test I use starts with 6-pound line and ranges up to 10 pounds
for all but muskie fishing. There I jump up to 15-pound line.

Those figures do not, of course, include fly-rod fishing, in
which tapered leaders are used decreasing to as little as, for
some trout fishing, 1-pound tippets.

Most monofilament line has a long "shelf-life." That is to
say, it does not deteriorate much sitting on the dealer's shelf
before being sold.

By the same token, most monofilament line is weakened
by being severely stretched, as would happen in the joyful
event that the angler caught a lot of big, long-fighting fish.

Unless nicked by snags or careless handling, most good grades of mono fishing line will last for at least two seasons, depending largely upon how much use and strain they have sustained.

Beyond two years it is penny-wise and pound-foolish to push your luck. Fishing trips usually cost enough to warrant guaranteeing success by having good line on all reels.

Twisted fishing line: Some fishing lures tend to spin and will, in time, twist any fishing line into a useless mass of kinks. This is especially true of the monofilament line on spinning reels. When twists become noticeable, it usually is too late to avoid some line damage since severe twisting weakens the line strength.

To avoid such mishaps, let your line trail behind the moving boat while underway to the fishing grounds. No weight should be put on the line. Instead, it should be fed out behind the moving boat, by hand if necessary, until enough line drag is created to pull it off the reel.

If you let about half of the line trail behind the boat for ten minutes or more, you can be assured that all or most of the twist will be removed.

Reel the line in again when ready, but be sure the last few yards are reeled in with finger-pressure on the line to avoid loose coils. The line drag will be more than enough to keep the line taut while a lot of it is still overboard. It is only when most of the line has been reeled in that line drag is lost.

A stitch in time: Regardless of what kind of fishing you are doing, after each strike, whether or not the fish is hooked and landed, double-check the hook point and the line or leader for at least two feet above the hook or lure.

This applies especially to those delicate hooks used for tying trout flies. Often the tempering of such hooks is off by only a tiny bit, but it can be enough to make the points and barbs brittle. Many a good trout rise has been missed because the preceding trout has broken the hook point off.

Likewise, many a good fish has been lost because the last fish dragged the line or leader over a sharp rock or snag and nicked it just enough to reduce the test strength by half or, perhaps, even more.

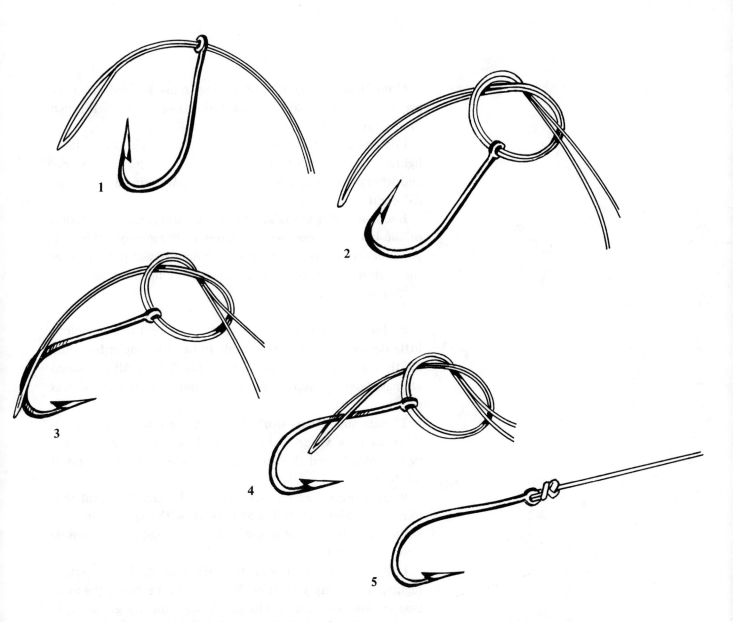

*Double assurance knot
for securing monofilament lines
or leaders to hooks*

By running the last few feet of the line or leader between your thumb and forefinger you can feel for nicks. Any roughness indicates a nick. Cut the line or leader off above the nick, then retie the line, or replace the leader.

Knot-tying: Because today's anglers seem to prefer monofilament lines—and for sound reasons—each knot tied should be carefully snugged down against itself by the thumbnail and forefinger.

Failure to solidly set each knot, including testing them by strong, steady pulls, too often results in slippage and loss of good fish.

Monofilament line is slippery and must be tied in an approved knot to hold without losing line strength through "knot-pinching."

For smokers, touching the cut end of each knot with a lighted cigarette will melt a small "blob" of the line material and form an insurance ball against slip-out during a prolonged fish-fight.

Recommended knots are displayed throughout this section of the book. Through wide use over a full range of fishing experiences, those shown have been found to adequately cover the majority of fishing needs. Practice tying them until perfection is assured each time.

Flyline-to-leader knot: There are two or three ingenious little devices on the market made to help the angler to secure his fly leader to the casting end of his flyline. All are aimed at making the junction point as smooth and unobtrusive as possible.

Though such items work, I have an aversion to using them. With my poor vision and my lack of skill in fishing wet flies or nymphs, I need the obvious bulge of a knot on the end of my flyline.

When fishing wet flies or nymphs, I watch the knot that joins my leader to my line as it floats with the current. Rare is the trout strike that doesn't jerk that small but still visible knot and warn me.

I tie a loop in the leader, then tie it on the flyline with a regular, four-wrap jam knot. When drawn up tight, the junction of line and leader will go through the tip guide easily enough and still be visible when floating on the water.

Dry-fly dressing: Before redressing a dry fly that has been mouthed by a trout or has been sucked under by turbulence and soaked, false cast the fly on a shortened line for about 30 seconds—make sure it doesn't hit the water.

By false casting the fly you will dry all excess water off the fly hackles. The redressing will be most effective when excess water has been removed.

Improved jam knot

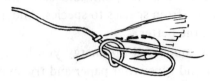  

*Improved knot
for tying on streamers*

Blood knot for tying fly leaders

FISHING

Noise pollution: With the exception of trout (the freshwater variety), boat noises, including engine exhausts, rarely if ever have a measurable effect on fishing success that lasts more than a few minutes after the noise ceases.

I can recall that when my father was teaching me to fish, at the tender and impressionable age of six, his constant reminders to speak softly and avoid thumping the bottom of the boat were a standard part of each trip. In fact, as memory serves me now, it seems that he made more noise warning me than I made at my worst.

Those were the days before "enlightenment" via scuba-diving studies of the effect of noise on game fish.

Today we know that sustained noise levels will spook fish. We know that the thrashing of a high-speed boat propeller will drive fish away in shallow water. But we also have learned that any moderately cautious approach to a fishing spot will be more than adequate to avoid alarming whatever is present at that time and in that location.

On the opposite side of that coin, trout, especially those in small streams, can be spooked into rigid refusal of all flies for hours by the vibrations of a heavy foot along the stream banks. This is especially true of quiet, clear pools where trout can often be seen but not caught.

263

Setting the hook: Assuming the use of needle-sharp hooks—and that is something you should always be certain of—the amount of force it takes to sink the point and barb into a fish's jaw varies considerably from species to species. And, for most fish, the more force, the better.

As an example of how much rod-tip energy you have to exert, take any piece of bond typewriter paper and try an experiment with it.

Have a friend hold the paper stretched between his hands with one edge level. Carefully lay a hook on the top edge of the paper, then back off about 50 or more feet and try to drive the point of the hook through the paper: First take up the slack and, with a flip of the rod tip, simulate setting the hook in a fish's jaw.

An old southern largemouth-bass (he calls them "bigmouth") fisherman I know advised me to "set that hook hard enough to cross his eyes, then do it again to be sure."

For bass that is good advice unless you are using light fly-rod equipment and low-test leaders. For bait- or plug-casting gear and spinning tackle the warning to set the hook hard will prevent many disappointing losses of big bass.

Double-setting the hook is good practice for all but trout fishing; and that includes sea trout (weakfish), which have soft mouths like their freshwater cousins.

As long as the reel drag-setting is correct there is nothing to lose and everything to gain by double-setting the hook after that first strike.

Playing a big fish: One of the most persistent common denominators among all types of sport fishing is the skill involved in fighting a big fish, be it a big bluegill or a record marlin.

The major key to success in this league can be described as "constant but controlled pressure on the line at all times after the first strike."

For heavy fish in the big-game category the pump-and-reel method is most often used. Once the fish is solidly hooked, this requires that the angler alternately lift the rod tip, then carefully lower it while reeling in line fast enough to keep pressure on the line. The slightest interruption in pressure may cost the loss of a good fish.

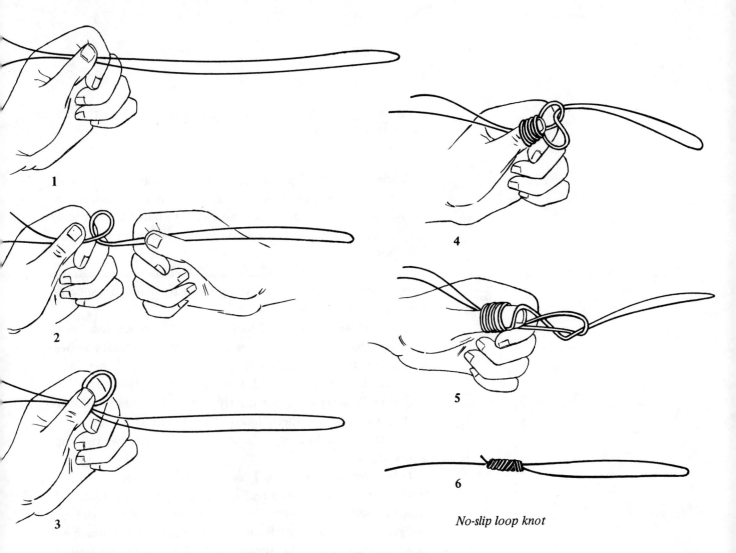

No-slip loop knot

As the line is reeled in after lifting the rod tip, the tip must be allowed to dip downward again as the line pressure calls for it. By maintaining a good bend in the rod you can be assured of line pressure.

When fighting a big fish, never allow the rod or line tension to relax for an instant.

Fighting freshwater fish of all species is best done with the rod tip held high. This will keep rod pressure on the line as the rod bends with each lunge of the fish. By reeling in in coordination with the rod-bend you will soon exhaust even the biggest fish.

For such feisty freshwater antagonists as muskies, the same pump-and-reel technique used for big-game fish will be found useful.

Unless there is danger of breaking the rod—which should never happen if the drag is set properly and if the line strength is not more than the rod can stand—never allow the rod tip to lower enough so that it points at the fish and allows the rod to "unflex" its built-in power.

A sneaky trout trick: Once, when I had watched the same young man walk away from a local trout stream three days in a row with his limit of trout, I asked him what his secret was. He smiled, or grinned would be more accurate, and said: "Salmon eggs."

Phooey! I had seen salmon eggs used often enough to know there had to be something more to that kid's success than just salmon eggs.

The next week I watched him at work. He took a few salmon eggs from his jar and tossed them in the stream above where he stood on the bank. Then he just stood there and watched them disappear with the current.

Suddenly he picked up his fly rod and baited the hook with a salmon egg, then tossed it upstream as he had done with the nonhooked eggs. In mere seconds he was fighting a nice trout.

Later, when I told him I had watched his technique, he smiled (that time it was a real smile, not a grin) and admitted that he used the free-floating eggs to locate trout. Once having seen a trout zip out from its hiding place to grab a free-floating salmon egg, he simply offered the next one with a hook in it. How's that for typical "kid-logic"?

His hooks were number 18, extremely short-shanked "salmon-egg-hooks," and he rarely missed a strike.

Fish bags: The unmatched best way to keep fish after they have been caught is alive. There are several ways of accomplishing that aim. The best known are the numerous varieties of fish stringers made of heavy cord, light rope, chain, or chain covered with rubber.

Then there are the open-meshed laundry bags. When laced at the open end with heavy cord so they can be closed securely, they make the finest of all fish keepers.

Granted, even the largest of laundry bags has size limitations in terms of the type of fish that can be kept alive overboard. But for the rather wide use-range they do have, there is no better solution to keeping your catch "live-fresh."

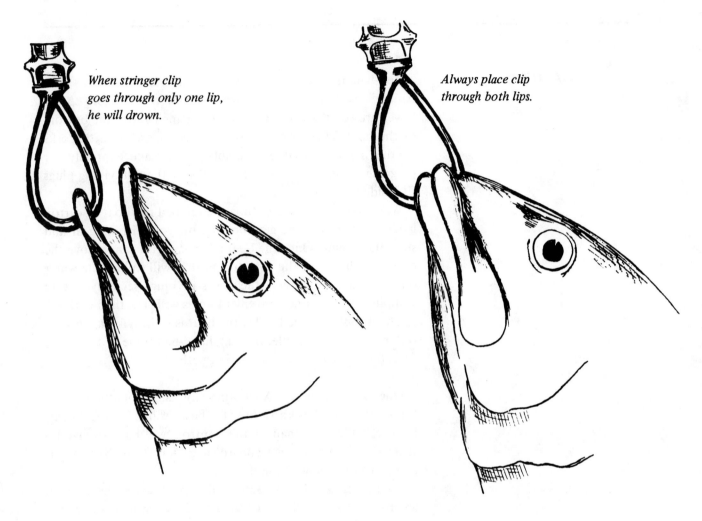

When stringer clip goes through only one lip, he will drown.

Always place clip through both lips.

To keep them alive longer

Even relatively close-meshed laundry bags can be used if a number of small holes are cut in the sides to permit sufficient exchange of water so the fish do not suffocate.

By tying the mouth of the laundry bag to the gunwale of the boat and lifting it into the boat each time you wish to move to a new location, you assure the delicate taste that accompanies really fresh fish.

BOATING

Self-bailers: Any small fishing boat can be made "self-bailing" by boring one or two holes in the transom so the lower arcs of the holes are about one inch above the bottom of the boat. Then you can use either commercial bottle corks or the manufactured expandable types made expressly for plugging self-bailing holes. The corks or the self-bailing plugs fit inside the boat, not outside.

When you find your outboard-equipped rowboat or cartop laden with rainwater, get aboard with your fishing gear and start the engine. Once the boat is moving you can remove the corks or plugs and the forward motion will siphon the water out. Be sure to replace the corks or plugs securely before stopping, or the same convenient holes will sink the boat.

This should not be tried if the boat is so heavily laden with water that it is unstable. Instead, hand-bail some of the water first, then proceed with the easier method.

One-man anchoring: Anchoring any fishing boat in exactly the right spot takes know-how for best results. This frequently means that the man at the controls will have to give instructions to a passenger aboard or get up from the controls and place the anchor himself.

By rigging a suitably large pulley on the foredeck or on an installed bowsprit, you can run the anchor line over the pulley and back to the stern or the control center where the captain can handle it himself. While the boat is underway the anchor can be snubbed up tight to prevent bumping the boat. If waves are too high, the anchor can be easily brought aboard for safer stowage.

Life-jacket stowage: Federal boating safety laws now require that one approved life jacket be kept aboard for each person in the boat. Convenient stowage of those vital but bulky objects often is a problem, especially in small boats.

Hardware stores, marine supply houses, tackle shops, and even some auto-supply stores carry heavy elastic "tie-downs," equipped with a hook at each end. These tie-downs can be used in conjunction with screw eyes to safely stow life jackets

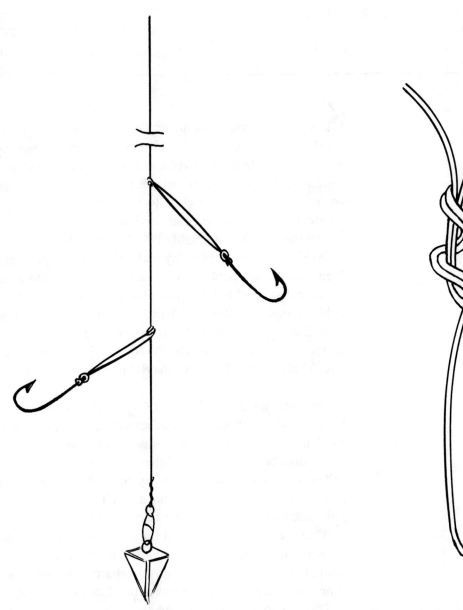

Knot used to make dual-hook bottom fishing rigs

under the boat seat or along the inside of the boat, whichever is more convenient.

Buy tie-downs long enough to do the job; then install screw eyes far enough apart so that the jackets will be held firmly by the elastic tie-downs. If the life jackets are needed, the occupants of the boat can easily reach the tie-downs and free the jackets quickly.

Keeping live minnows alive: Two things contribute significantly to the loss of live minnows while being transported or while fishing: lack of oxygen and rising water temperatures. Because rising water temperatures hasten the loss of dissolved oxygen in water, the trick is to keep the temperature down where it belongs for best bait survival.

The inexpensive and highly popular styrofoam coolers available almost everywhere today make the best baitkeepers ever. You can fill the cooler with water, and if you add a supply of ice cubes or chunk-ice in a plastic bag, the ice will keep it cold enough to assure live bait for a day or more. Minnows should be put in the cooler at the same time the ice is put in so that they will get used to the lowering temperature gradually. This will avoid loss by what is known as "thermal shock."

Crayfish "magic": Whether they are known in the reader's territory as crayfish, crawfish, crawdads, dads, or any other local name, there is a way to use live crayfish for bass bait that works better than most other ways.

The trick was taught to me by one George Bloomenauer, a senior citizen who has caught more big smallmouth bass in Potomac River than any other two men I know.

What George does is to peel the first hard shell section, just back of the head, before baiting the hook. This exposes the white meat under the shell and, for whatever reason, is several times more attractive to smallmouths than the unpeeled dads.

Those who may be inclined to doubt the effectiveness of George's method should try to outfish him.

Onion chum bag: Many prepacked fresh vegetables sold in food markets come in large-weave plastic bags similar to the old-fashioned onion bags of bygone years. Though such bags are not very sturdy over the long haul, they can be carefully untied, emptied, and later used as chum bags.

For those who may not know what chum bags are, they are any open-weave, sacklike bag into which cut-up or ground fish, crabs, worms, and such may be put. Chum bags are lowered overboard on lines tied to the fishing boat. The chum in

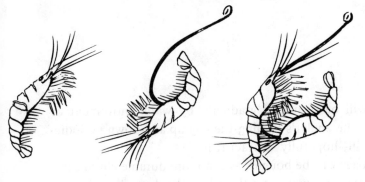

Grass shrimp,
the best all-around
live bait to use
for striped bass.

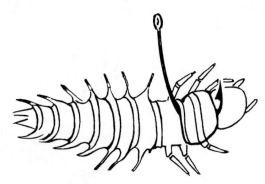

Hellgrammites are prime
bass bait. They should be hooked
behind the collar.

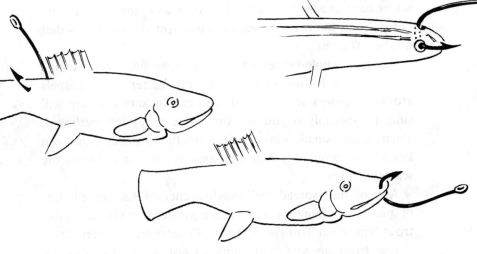

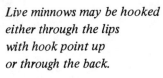

Live eels used as bait
for striped bass
stay alive longer
if hooked through the eyes.

Live minnows may be hooked
either through the lips
with hook point up
or through the back.

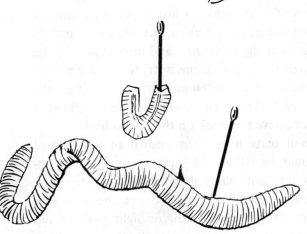

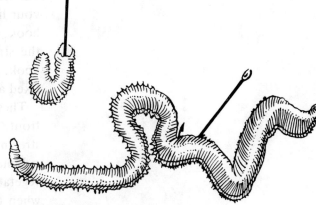

Night crawlers are prime bait
for all freshwater fish.
Smaller fish, such as sunfish,
prefer small pieces. Bass and other
larger fish prefer the whole worm.

Bloodworms are creatures
of the sea and are good bait
only for saltwater fish.
They may be used in small pieces
for small fish, but larger fish,
such as striped bass, prefer
the whole worm.

the bag will be dispersed gradually by water movement or simply by the angler's jiggling the bag up and down periodically and will—hopefully—attract fish.

Chum bags can be bought, as can more durable chum cans. But the free ones work as well and can be discarded when no longer useful.

Raiding the food locker: I am not sure whether America's fish have changed their feeding habits or the Americans themselves have changed their food. Either way, there are a number of food items now found in most American pantries that double efficiently as fish bait.

Canned, whole-kernel corn is sure-fire bait for catching carp, wherever they may be. If you scatter a few kernels around the area to be fished, you can be sure the carp will find it, especially if you first dump the corn juice overboard. Then, using small hooks, carefully thread on enough corn kernels to completely hide the hook and toss it in among the scattered corn.

Any of the "spreadable" cheddar cheeses that come in jars or plastic containers can be made into extremely successful trout bait where bait-fishing for freshwater trout is permitted.

Use trout hooks (short-shanked) not larger than number 12. Remove a portion of cheese about the size of the nail on your little finger from the container, and mold it around the hook. Even though the cheese seems soft, the cold water of the stream will cause it to stiffen enough to keep it on the hook, except in swift water. Use a small piece of split-shot fixed about a foot above the hook on the line or leader.

These cheeseball baits have been known to take record trout. They should be fished the same as worms—cast upstream and allowed to drift naturally with the current.

Believe it or not, cooked elbow macaroni can be dyed with vegetable coloring (either red, green, or light yellow) and when threaded carefully on small hooks will take trout. After cooking and dyeing the macaroni, drain it thoroughly and store in a tightly capped jar for use not more than two days later. Make only enough for each trip, to avoid wasting the family's food supply.

Flour, water, anisette, and cottonballs are the ingredients for taking either carp or catfish. Each cottonball should be

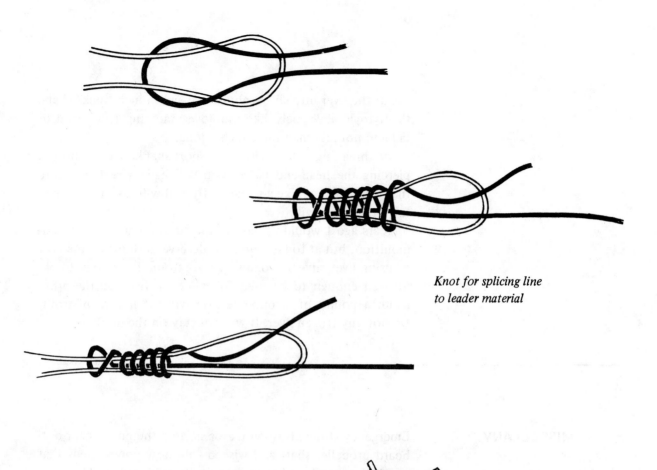

*Knot for splicing line
to leader material*

snipped in half. When your supply of halved cottonballs is large enough, prepare the following mix:

Mix flour and water until a pastelike consistency is achieved. Next add a few drops of anisette, available in drugstores and food markets. Mix again thoroughly, then take one half-cottonball at a time and with the fingers knead in the mixture until it is saturated. Roll gently between thumb and forefinger to make a ball and set aside to dry.

When the "doughballs" are dry, store them in any box or bait can for future use. To avoid losing the anisette flavor, keep the storage container tightly closed.

I confess that I first saw the following idea used back in the days when fresh liver could be bought for about 40 cents a pound. If you dare use liver at today's prices, use it in the way described in the following paragraphs.

Cut the liver into slivers about one-eighth inch thick. Shape them to look vaguely like minnows, tapering from head to tail and not less than three inches long.

By threading a liver sliver on short-shanked trout hooks, piercing the head-end twice, you will have a real-meat lure that can be fished like a streamer fly and will take trout when few other lures will.

Years ago I wouldn't have bothered to include this last admonition, but at today's prices it deserves a thought: the cost of using liver slivers is one sliver per trout. They do not hold up well enough to be used for a second fish. On the other hand, a pound of second-rate liver will catch a lot of trout. Do not buy frozen liver. It will not stay on the hook.

MISCELLANY

Emergency stores: Have you ever sheared the pin in your outboard propeller shaft and wished—oh, how you wished—that you had remembered to keep extra shear pins aboard?

Shear pins are not the only frequently forgotten emergency items. The list includes first-aid equipment, screwdrivers, at least one adjustable wrench, adhesive tape to replace a rod guide that gets knocked off or comes loose—the list goes on and on.

Most hardware stores offer storage drawers of many suitable sizes, usually made of plastic. They come in sets that include drawer slides and screws for mounting them. By installing one or more of these drawers under the boat seats you can keep emergency equipment always aboard where it will be ready when needed.

Lure-saver: When underwater lures or plugs get snagged, they seldom can be retrieved by pulling on the line. More times than not this will only dig the hook points in deeper and lessen the chances of retrieving your $2 or $3 lure.

A solution to this dilemma is a piece of equipment that can be made at home. Use a piece of two-inch diameter aluminum tubing about four inches long, fill the tube with molten lead, and allow it to cool.

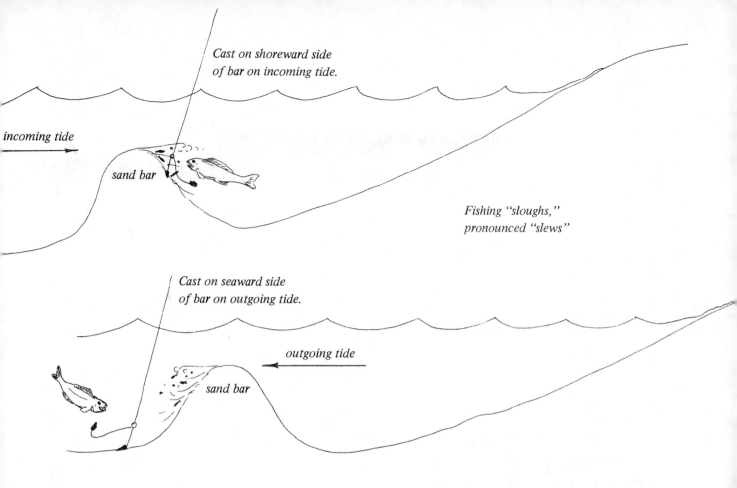

Cast on shoreward side of bar on incoming tide.

incoming tide

sand bar

Fishing "sloughs," pronounced "slews"

Cast on seaward side of bar on outgoing tide.

outgoing tide

sand bar

Attach two screw eyes, one at each end, on one side of the lead-filled tube. Using pliers, carefully open each screw eye slightly, just enough to allow you to slip your fishing line into the eyes. In one end attach a strong screw eye to which has been tied a suitably long length of heavy twine.

The next time you snag a lure or plug on the bottom, slip the line into the two slightly open screw eyes and allow the weight to slide down the line and bump the snagged lure. By lifting and bumping the snagged lure while trying the line to see if it is free, you can save the snagged plug about nine times out of ten.

Handy lure storage: Because bass fishermen are among the greatest "lure changers" in the fishing fraternity, a handy gadget to have aboard bass-fishing boats is a strip (or as many as are needed) of waste styrofoam packing either taped or tacked in a convenient location inside the gunwale of the boat. By taking selected lures or plugs out of the tackle box ahead of time, you can stick the hooks in the styrofoam plastic for safe storage until they are needed.

This eliminates opening and closing the tackle box in the usually crowded confines of the average bass-fishing boat.

Chapter twenty-one

Tackle selection

Buying fishing tackle for any type of fishing is an event that should be approached with some forethought.

The basic pieces for which the largest initial outlay of cash will be made are rods, reels, and lines. Everything else should be considered secondary.

It is important to realize from the beginning that there is no such thing as an "all-purpose" rod-reel-line combination. Nevertheless, it is possible to select one combination that will cover all the fishing needs of an individual angler whose fishing ambitions or circumstances are *limited to freshwater species.*

Saltwater fishing is another story. There you will find such a broad variety of fishing, and such an equally wide range of tackle needs, that no one outfit could possibly serve all types of fishing with any degree of efficiency.

Whereas most freshwater rods, reels, and lines may upon occasion be used in salt or brackish water, the reverse will probably never be true. If or when freshwater tackle is used in salt water it must be thoroughly washed with fresh water and mild soap immediately after being used each day to prevent salt corrosion from ruining it. That can happen overnight.

Except for individuals to whom money is no problem, cost must be considered. But cost should not be the primary factor in making a choice.

Today's fishing-tackle market has evolved into a jumble of discounted prices to a point where there literally is no such thing as a realistic retail price that cannot be bettered someplace. Much discount pricing is the result of carload buying on the part of big chain stores, who have the purchasing power to buy in huge quantities and thus reduce their own cost. In too many instances, however, the old "let the buyer beware" warning prevails.

*Cheap buying
is chancy buying*

Prospective buyers should be aware that advertised sales of name-brand tackle are often used as "leaders" to lure the unwary into stores where much of the inventory falls short of being top grade; where second-rate imitations of the real thing often are priced above what they could be bought for elsewhere.

Experienced anglers usually are wise to tackle-trade tricks. Most of them made a few early mistakes themselves. They steer clear of come-on gimmicks or sales pitches.

For the novice angler the best place to go for that all-important initial outlay is the local tackle shop. The proprietors of such relatively small retail tackle shops usually know their business because they are fishermen themselves. Moreover, their main stock in trade, the one thing that lets them stay in business against fearful odds imposed by discounting chain stores, is their ability to advise the angler and service what they sell.

277

In addition, since most local tackle shops are part of the communities in which they are located, the owners do everything possible to merit buyer respect and confidence.

In the realm of freshwater fishing tackle there are numerous price ranges, from expensive to cheap. Most will serve their purpose if not used beyond the quality limits imposed by the purchase price.

It would, however, be penny-wise and pound-foolish to buy a rod-reel-line combination, solely on a price basis, in the face of contrary recommendations from the local dealer. If the dealer knows how you intend to use it, he will not want to sell you an outfit that will fail to measure up to the job. That way he could lose the one thing he cannot afford to lose—a steady customer.

In freshwater equipment, really expensive tackle rarely functions any better than tackle in the medium price range. Too often the increased cost of such equipment is due solely to adornment or status-symbol considerations rather than to a real upgrading in efficiency.

Saltwater tackle is a different story. Because it must be made corrosion-proof and usually must be more sturdy than freshwater gear, most saltwater-tackle costs jump from cheap to expensive—with a corresponding jump in quality. There is very little in between.

Second-rate saltwater fishing reels fail most frequently in the drag mechanisms—usually when you are fighting the biggest fish you've ever hooked. That is when a flawless drag is of prime importance.

Because it is a very competitive business, most reputable name-brand rod, reel, and line manufacturers back their products with guarantees or warrantees sufficient to assure the buyer's getting his money's worth from their equipment.

It might be argued that part of the cost of name-brand tackle results from the size of budgets for nationwide advertising in outdoor magazines. That may be true, but what few buyers realize is that because of the volume of sales produced by those ads, the advertising cost per item is very low, not very high.

For whatever comfort it may provide the first-time tackle buyer, there is very little *really* shoddy fishing tackle on the legitimate tackle market today.

In freshwater rods, reels, and lines, the closest approach to an all-around outfit is spinning gear. Second on the list would be fly-fishing tackle, third, bait- or plug-casting tackle.

A balanced medium-action spinning rod, reel, and line combination can be used for everything in the freshwater fishing category except, perhaps, muskellunge and dry-fly trout fishing.

A balanced fly rod, reel, and line can be used for everything except muskies (and there have been muskies caught on fly rods) and deepwater bait fishing.

A plug- or bait-casting rod, reel, and line can be used for bass and numerous other freshwater fish that take plugs or spoons. Stout plug rods can even be used to take northern pike and muskies.

On the other side of the usefulness coin, you cannot expect to troll heavy lures for muskies or freshwater striped bass with a light- or medium-action spinning outfit. Before a fish strikes, the weight and water resistance of lures commonly used for those two species has already used up most of the rod and line strength.

Similarly, fly rods are not efficient for trolling because the resistance of the line dragging through the water imposes too much initial load on the rod.

Obviously, bait- or plug-casting rods and reels cannot be used to cast dry flies or lures made to be cast with spinning tackle. They are just too light to handle with a plug rod.

In all cases, both freshwater and saltwater tackle must be balanced. That is to say, the line and reel must balance the heft of the rod. That is especially true in fly-fishing equipment, as was noted in the chapter on trout fishing.

Balance is the key

For spinning and plug-casting, saltwater trolling, and surf-casting equipment, the test strength of the lines must not exceed the ability of the rods to use up to 90 percent of the line strength without breaking.

It would be equally out of balance to have such reels equipped with lines so light in test strength that they could not even approach the strength built into the rods.

All of the above points, and more, are best discussed with a local tackle dealer, especially for that first major purchase of rod, reel, and line.

Chapter twenty-two

"Ten Best" fishing locations

Without exception, every fisherman I have met and talked to for any length of time has eventually extolled the wonders of fishing at his own favorite locations. Often these tales of angling paradises are based on one or two trips that just happened to pan out better than any other in the angler's recent memory.

Listeners to such tales who are prompted to visit such cherished hot-spots frequently return less enchanted than the taleteller. But that's fishing. There are days when even the most skilled hook-flingers in the best fishing spots will draw blanks.

By way of example, Bill and Alice Bristor have been arranging our annual trout trips to Shavers Fork, West Virginia, for many years.

With the exception of one day, one year, all trips have been successes, with as many as 120 trout logged in the hooked-and-released category.

I say hooked and released because we always fish the catch-and-return section of Shavers, a 5½-mile stretch of pure trout fishing—the kind you read about but seldom actually experience.

Our annual foray to Shavers involves four days. We take as many friends along as possible. Our last trip included a total of six anglers: Bill and Alice, Steve Cohen and Neil Feldman (two novices), Doctor Wayne Jacobson, and me. The total score that time was over 140 trout legitimately hooked and released. None were less than 12 inches long and two weighed more than 4 pounds.

Hot fishing? You can bet your old granny's A.T. & T. stock. It is the best in the eastern United States.

Yet, when Ed Russell, Don Benson, and Boyd Pfeiffer fished Shavers Fork one year, a week after our trip, they came home asking if they had perhaps gotten lost and fished the wrong stream. As I recall, all three fly-fishing experts managed to total only five or six trout during their three-day stay. They haven't been back since.

Heavy rains can put the kazonk on trout fishing in Shavers Fork, if rain continues for more than a few hours, or if it rains two days in a row.

Bounded all around by solid rock formations, Shavers doesn't actually get muddy. It does get murky and high. Moreover, it gets dangerously fast and all but impossible to fish with anything but heavy spinning lures. And who goes to a trout stream equipped with heavy spinning lures, especially with the barbless hooks required by law?

So some fishermen are inclined to look askance at Shavers. Fortunately for several reputations, we have taken enough people there over the years to more than offset any out-spoken disdain of our fishing claims.

In the realm of freshwater fishing, Shavers Fork heads my top-ten list. Located on top of Shavers Mountain near Elkins, West Virginia, the stream really is the Shavers Fork of the Cheat River and runs through Monongahela National Forest.

To fish Shavers Fork, out-of-state anglers should plan to stop at a town called Bartow for 10-day tourist fishing licenses and a National Forest use-stamp. At last year's prices that would total $11 plus about 50 cents for agents' fees. The National Forest stamp is good for one year. The $10 tourist fishing license is an unequaled bargain. If you plan more than one trip, the year-round nonresident license is only $20.

Right on top of the mountain, facing National Forest property, is the only overnight eatery-and-sleepery, a fine hostel called the Pocohontas Motel, owned and operated by Dabney and Renie Kisner. Food is excellent and prices are reasonable.

More important, Pocohontas Motel is a gathering place for Shavers Fork fishermen. Dabney knows all the shortcut trails to the 5½-mile fish-for-fun area as well as to the other 30 miles of stocked waters divided on each end of the remotely located, barbless-hooks-only portion of the stream.

Though the fish-for-fun area limits the angler to "artificial flies and spinners equipped with barbless hooks," and though each angler may take only one trout per day over 18 inches long, the other 30 miles are open to bait fishing as well as to flies with barbed hooks and have a generous daily creel limit.

Fishermen in flocks

Weekends and holidays usually bring out more fishermen than the average trout buff likes to see at one time.

Midweek days, except for holidays, are the stuff of which dreams are made. In all of our annual treks to Shavers we have planned around weekdays and have never seen more than a dozen fishermen on the whole 5½-mile reach, counting our own parties.

The most productive dry fly for us has been the Royal Coachman, hair wing or Wulff-tied on a number 12 hook. Second best is the Irresistible, also on a number 12 hook.

Doc Jacobson carries number 14s with him but seldom has had to use them.

For underwater work the "Dabney Special," obviously available from Dabney Kisner only, works wonders in the deeper holes with a spinner ahead of it.

Bill and Alice, who have caught more big trout in Shavers than most trout fans ever see, favor the green inchworm for early season fishing prior to mid-June.

We have found from years of experience that June 11 or thereabouts is the prime time for us.

That date varies with the calendar and our midweek preferences. If you stick June 11 someplace in the middle of your visit you'll be right on for dates by our reckoning.

One reason for the seemingly late date is the 4500-foot elevation of Shavers Fork. Area residents have recorded snow on those mountains as late as May.

June is considered the best month for all-around trout fishing. July, August, and early September are what we call number-16-dry-fly months because that's what it takes to raise trout then—if the flies are tied on nothing heavier than 6-X tippets. Even bait fishermen in the open reaches of the stream have a tough time raising fish during the hot weeks.

Available on the fishing menu are brook, brown, rainbow, and golden trout. Bill and Alice, who together know Shavers better than they do their living-room floor, have over the years logged at least 30 trout over 18 inches long, six of which have exceeded 4 pounds. (Doubting Thomases who may be tempted to scoff will be shown color photos.)

Religiously careful of the trout, Bill never touches the fish to photograph them. Either he or Alice holds the hook or leader, or takes the Polaroid shots with the prizes in the net.

The first trip under Bill's guidance is sure to be an 11-mile, skip-fishing tour of the 5½-mile fish-for-fun section. After the newcomer has been shown all of Bill and Alice's favorite pools and slicks, he is on his own.

Any plans for Shavers Fork trips that include staying at Pocohontas Motel should be preceded by a phone call reservation to Dabney or Renie Kisner—area code 304, 456-4281. For those who prefer camping, there are ample regulated campsites and primitive camping spots in Monongahela National Forest. Personally, I greatly favor Renie's cooking over my own. And when Alice Bristor is fishing, you can't get her near a cookfire, so camping is out for us. More important, especially for those of us who have somewhat lost the youthful ability to rejuvenate on command, the restorative effects of a good bed after a day on Shavers are a must.

SANTEE-COOPER RESERVOIR

In the largemouth-bass fishing realm, the Santee-Cooper Reservoir in South Carolina is to bass fishing what the Florida Keys are to saltwater fishing. At least that's my opinion, which takes into account that other bass fans I know lay similar kind words on such noted places as Dale Hollow in Tennessee and Lake Seminole or the St. Johns River in Florida, to name a few that I've often heard praised.

Santee-Cooper Reservoir came into being as the present twin-lake impoundment after a dam was built in 1941 which blocked the flows from Santee River and Cooper River and formed two lakes, Marion and Moultrie, connected by a navigable diversion canal.

In addition to largemouth bass, striped bass trapped behind the dam have reproduced sufficiently to make up a landlocked striped-bass fishery that is the envy of every state fisheries department with similar lakes.

Despite its size (170,000 acres of water in the two lakes), it has been said that Santee-Cooper has more bass experts per acre than any similar bass haven in the country.

This is partly because all of the nation's best bass fishermen have swarmed to this relatively new find, and area service establishments have taken careful note of their results.

The best thing about Santee-Cooper in my book is the variety of bass water to be found. There is everything from perfect popping bug territory to the deeper reaches where bottom-crawling plugs are needed—plus plenty of in-between water where middle-depth plugs and big surface plugs will do the job.

To date my own visits have been limited to late May, but guides there say the fishing is good through June, usually, with a slack-off during July and August followed by another pickup in catches during the last week in September through the end of November. I chose May because Ray Anseaume, once the chief herald at this South Carolina bass Mecca, said it was the best of all times for bass.

At the time of my last visit the record was more than 10 pounds for largemouths and more than 35 pounds for stripers. I have since learned that both records have been beaten. I also have learned that numerous 10-pound bass have been logged and that the average runs over 6 pounds. Correct or not, anything near a 6-pound average for as many largemouths as are caught there each year is terrific bass fishing.

Accommodations range in price and comfort from primitive camping facilities to motels. Guides, boats, baits, motors, and free advice abound.

Compared to my first visit, the setup has lost some of the untouched mystique and natural charm that existed before everybody down there got married to the big tourist dollar. But considering what that place offers in the way of outstanding fishing, I've never heard anybody complain.

Smith Mountain Lake, Virginia, is included among my top ten spots, not because I have ever tapped a limit of bass there, but because I have seen live fish caught by others who got there a week or two ahead of me and who hit those ever-changing conditions smack on the nose.

Of all the bass waters I have fished, Smith Mountain Lake combines the best of everything for both largemouth and smallmouth bass-fishing territory. Now, since striped bass have been released in the lake, that species also is available, along with trout and northern pike.

Doc Jacobson and I have been to Cedar Key Lodge (now called Mountainhead Lodge since Leo and Hester Bourassa retired) at least a dozen times and have never hit conditions just right. We caught bass, some big. But Leo used to keep the really big bass in a spacious live-box to show skeptics like me what could be done if a man had the skill.

Paul Beyerle, who was Leo's chief bass guide, could take me out and put me on bass inside of 20 minutes from the dock. Once he even put me on a big northern that stripped my reel bare of line before Paul could gun the outboard fast enough to catch up to the fish.

Doc and I could go out and fish our heads off and come in at the end of the day with three or four bass in the 3- to 4-pound weight bracket.

To bolster our flagging enthusiasm, and I suspect also to wipe our eyes a bit, Paul and Leo made several trips together and brought back some of the real bass that lurk in Smith Mountain Lake.

One of the key features of the lake is the more than 550 miles of shoreline in the lake's 55-mile length. That adds up to an average of about 10 miles of cove, creek, and inlet shoreline for each linear mile of the lake. That also adds up to a heap of bass casting territory.

In spite of never having caught any bass big enough to raise Paul's eyebrows, I would willingly set out for Smith Mountain Lake now if it were May.

Though you'd think fate would deal more kindly with me, all of the people I have touted the lake to have caught a lot of bass and a few big ones. Having been raised on southern bayou "bigmouth" fishing, I'm not too ashamed of being less than top dog in the lake-fishing league. I obviously have a lot to learn—but at my age I could use a little acceleration in the learning process before I run out of fishing time.

CHESAPEAKE BAY

In a top-ten listing it is perhaps understandable that a man will tend to include his home waters, the regions he knows best.

Chesapeake Bay falls into the category of home waters for me. I would be remiss if I deliberately left it out just to avoid the charge of touting my home state. In point of fact, the Bay ranks among the top-ten of thousands of anglers, including me.

Approximately 185 miles long from its headwaters at the confluence of the Susquehanna River to its mouth at Cape Charles, Virginia, Chesapeake Bay is the east coast's largest "inland sea."

It has been called the striped-bass factory of the east coast, for it furnishes spillover stripers that migrate out of the bay and range both north and south along the Atlantic Ocean's inshore waters.

286

Each year the commercial catch of striped bass in the bay amounts to about 4 million pounds. The sport-fishing catch is easily as large if not larger.

At the peak of the chumming season it is common to see from 200 to 500 charter and private boats anchored at whatever hot spots are working at the time. By day's end each of those boats will have as many as 150 stripers, called rockfish here, in the fish boxes. During "big-fish-years" those stripers will average about 5 pounds each.

Dependable action usually gets under way in mid-May for early trollers seeking fish in the 20- to 50-pound weight range.

I saw one fish that tore up a gill net before being captured and killed. It tipped the scales at 100 pounds, 1 ounce, on an official scale. I was with state biologists when they trapped stripers migrating through the Chesapeake and Delaware Canal and helped to weigh, measure, and release specimens that topped 75 pounds. The current state record for hook-and-line catches stands at 54 pounds.

Besides all its striped-bass abundance and their May-through-November availability most years, the bay has other attractions to offer.

During the high swing of Atlantic Ocean bluefish population cycles, Chesapeake Bay plays host to massive invasions of these spectacular fighters.

Though their abundance varies with the total oceanic population, few years have been recorded when the blues failed to make their mark on summer fishing.

In 1974 the bluefish invasion hit a peak never before equaled for numbers and average size in the bay. Fish in the 15- to 20-pound range savaged in schools on and around all known feeding shoals. Smaller versions in the 6- to 10-pound range were everywhere. Later in the season, about mid-August, a few schools of still smaller blues showed up and then disappeared, perhaps becoming food for the big ones.

Striper success for the year diminished sharply as most anglers rigged for blues. Moreover, it is believed that the massive presence of big bluefish chased the less-aggressive stripers into hiding.

Some of the real striper experts among the bay's sizable charter fleet managed to take plenty of fish on drifted soft-crab baits, but the total still was less than for previous years.

As though on signal to fill a need, huge schools of menhaden, or alewives, moved into the bay and pushed all the way up to Susquehanna Flats into fresh water. Except for the abundance of those food fish, Chesapeake Bay's basic striper population might have been damaged by predation and starvation. But good fortune apparently continues to smile on these waters. Biologists do not look for any serious decrease in striper fishing as a result of the bluefish invasion.

Along with the blues of '74 came equally unusual numbers of sea trout. They were both abundant and larger than normal, 7- and 8-pounders being common.

As part of the justification for my enthusiasm over Chesapeake Bay fishing, the 1974 bonanza was only slightly better than normal fishing in 1973 and 1972.

Put another way, if the bonanza year of 1974 were to be rated as "one" on a one-to-ten scale, normal bay abundance would be only three places down the list.

Another mark of the popularity of Chesapeake Bay fishing can be found in the fact that few if any charterboats go unbooked, especially during the height of the season from June through September. Most of the better-known skippers are totally booked as much as a year in advance with a waiting list to call in case of cancellations. It is common practice among the more affluent anglers for one man to commit himself to a full season's booking with one captain. He will then fill out the up-to-six parties from among his own list of friends, business acquaintances, and so forth.

As is normal these days, prices have, in my opinion, gotten out of hand. Some of the best captains are getting from $125 to $150 per day for their services. But if the oil and other industries can get away with reaping windfall profits at the public's expense, one can hardly blame charter captains for doing the same thing on a smaller scale.

A final kudo for Chesapeake Bay: there are few places, including the Florida Keys, where better light-tackle saltwater sport will be found for both resident and migratory game fish. Both bluefish and stripers can be taken on light- to medium-action spinning tackle when they surface to feed in huge, voracious schools. Similar light-tackle sport is available by chumming, jigging with bucktail jigs, drifting live eels, and drifting soft crabs.

Imagine, if you can, taking really big stripers on light spinning or plug-casting rigs using jigs cast smack against the concrete pilings of the two bay-bridge spans. My first trip of the 1974 season with Mike Listorti and Mel Smith, two fishing firefighters, was distinguished by a 28½-pound striper hooked and landed less than a dozen casts after we had arrived at the span pilings. The smallest fish we caught that day was an 11-pounder and fishermen all around us were doing nearly as well.

For economic reasons only, fishing in the Florida Keys falls out of the number-one position. Where it rightfully belongs is a matter for the individual to decide, based on his pocketbook and his personal fishing preferences.

As shown in the Florida Keys Fishing Timetable found on pages 236-242, fishing there ranges from good to excellent for visitors who have never been exposed to the best the Keys have to offer.

For natives of the area, immune as they have become to what we outsiders would call fantastic fishing, no doubt the off periods in the angling schedule appear to warrant a "poor" rating.

I confess to having been bothered by heat and insects during some of my summer visits to the Keys, but with advance preparations, such as insect repellents, conditions have always been well within the tolerable range. Fishing has always been in my personal opinion "excellent," and at the worst level has still rated a "good" from me. This point is noted here to encourage anyone who has an opportunity for a quick trip, even in the so-called off-season.

The word may have reached you that some of the Keys fishing guides are charging prices that fall into the rip-off bracket. That is at least partly true. But not all guides are that greedy. Moreover, some of the higher-priced guides have learned that accepting a fair daily out-of-season fee from anglers who cannot afford in-season prices is better than sitting at the docks gazing out across the water.

Colleagues who have never fished the Keys have asked me if guides really are necessary. A general answer would have to be "Yes." That yes can be tempered by a number of circumstances, such as the fishing skills of the visiting anglers, the amount of time allotted to fishing the Keys, or the ability to pay for one guided trip designed to inform as much as possible. There are guides in the Keys who will cooperate with a candidly stated aim of that kind. I must add, however, that there are guides who will not cooperate but who may seem to do so.

On the opposite side of the coin, if you have enough time to make a few mistakes and perhaps waste a day or two fishing for the wrong fish in the right spots, it would be difficult to leave the Keys disappointed.

Most bait and tackle dealers throughout the 180-some miles from Miami to Key West are willing to give solid fishing information to anyone who asks for it. Rarely is such information wrong. More often than not, a bait and tackle dealer will give information on the fishing to be found around his own Key. All are wise to the value of word-of-mouth recommendations when visiting anglers get home again.

One good source of preplanning information is the Metropolitan-Miami Fishing Tournament, Miami Herald, Miami, Florida. Sponsored by the Miami Herald newspaper, the tourney offers a booklet that can be a big help if studied.

Among the list of state agencies to contact for fishing information on pages 301-308 is an address for Florida fishing. A note to that source would be best before finalizing plans.

The final admonition is: if you can afford a trip to the Keys, take it.

THE CAROLINA COAST

The coastal regions of both North Carolina and South Carolina offer such a variety of fishing opportunities that it would be difficult to list them all in these pages.

The first trip to either area should be made with an open mind, even if you think you are sure what kind of sport fishing you prefer.

As an added attraction for more northern anglers, much of the best sport fishing in both areas occurs during the off-season periods for northern waters.

Both states have developed agencies or organizations charged with the responsibility of seeing that all inquiries concerning fishing are answered—in full and glorious detail. A letter of request to either or both state agencies, listed elsewhere in this book, will bring results that may remind you of the man who, when asked for the time of day, would tell the time and then add full instructions on how to build your own watch.

Both states publish and offer fishing guide books crammed with attractively packaged articles on every kind of available fishing.

Before buying any tackle specifically for North or South Carolina, check the information books. Standard surf-fishing tackle, including surf spinning gear, will cover a wide variety of the available fishing. Purchases of terminal tackle, lures, and baits should be delayed to check local preferences upon arrival.

Overnight or longer accommodations are abundant and range in price from primitive camping to the best in motel and hotel facilities.

Both regions rate second in my book only to the Florida Keys, and that by the slimmest of margins. What's more, overall costs are considerably less.

Grand Isle, Louisiana, falls well within the top-ten listing by way of variety, abundance, and easy accessibility.

GRAND ISLE

Grand Isle has been known as a sport fisherman's paradise for generations, offering rustic simplicity, excellent and varied catches of typical Gulf game fish, and expert charter captains.

Though some environmentalists may wish to take issue with the point, the best fishing to be had off Grand Isle will be found at and around the offshore oil-drilling rigs, many of which are in sight of the beach.

Shortly after the drilling rigs sprouted from the floor of the Gulf, towering over the water on their steel legs, charter skippers discovered that instead of having to run miles offshore to find the best game fish all they had to do was learn how to fish the rigs.

This they accomplished in a hurry. And why not? All the fish they could imagine were suddenly available, in some cases even to small boat fishing.

Make no mistake, this is not light-tackle fishing. Instead, the best equipment would be in the medium to heavy boat-rod categories, either in spinning or conventional rod-and-reel combinations.

Because Louisiana has long been a favored bass state for me I have visited there many times. It was on one such jaunt that I first heard about Grand Isle and vowed to return the following year equipped with something stouter than my fly rod and spinning tackle.

Thanks to advice from friends who had sampled the Grand Isle sport, I went adequately equipped. Left to my own devices I would have been woefully undergunned to cover the whole range of possibilities.

A letter to the Louisiana fisheries authorities (see the listing of state agencies elsewhere in this book) should include a request for specific information about Grand Isle.

As one writer put it: "The number of words written extolling the virtues of oil-rig fishing off Grand Isle has been exceeded only by the number of barrels of oil produced by those rigs."

FLORIDA LAKES

Lochloosa Lake and its companion, Lake Orange, are located in north Florida between Gainesville and Ocala.

Both lakes are ringed by cypress and live oaks standing grotesquely beautiful, festooned with spanish moss and knee-deep in the typical brown water of most cypress swamps.

Though the natives of the area greatly prefer to fish for calicos (crappies), visitors are more inclined to go after the abundant and often huge largemouth bass in residence among the cypress trees.

On one trip to Lochloosa, Lefty Kreh and I brought an 8½-pounder back to the dock in the live well to show Hank Brenes, the dock owner, our success. To us "Yankee" bass anglers, an 8½-pound largemouth was bragging material. Hank, who had spent 22 years of his life running a fishing camp on the lake, didn't even raise his eyebrows.

To prove his point he took us into the clubhouse and opened his walk-in cooler where he had six bass hanging on hooks, all caught two days before by a group of local bass experts. Not one weighed less than 10 pounds.

Lake Harris and Little Lake Harris, near the town of Yalaha in north-central Florida, are another pair of bass lakes rated only fair among locals. To anglers used to nothing bigger or better than northern bass, the two bodies of water are purely astonishing.

Guided by Art Hutt, a Florida fishing authority and outdoor writer, we easily logged a triple-limit catch of largemouths in one afternoon using red plastic worms as cast-and-retrieve lures among the lakes' myriad weed beds.

As I noted in the beginning of this chapter, favorite fishing locations may come on strong for one man and weak for another. It depends on that all-important first impression.

It is a fact that between the best and the worst there are literally hundreds of both freshwater and saltwater fishing opportunities that are almost as good as the best.

It's a case of each to his own.

Chapter twenty-three

Fishing philosophy, a modern need

From the kid equipped only with a bent pin, a willow switch, and a length of his mother's sewing thread to the big-game fisherman riding the fighting chair of a $200,000 offshore sport-fishing cruiser, the urge to fish for and catch fish by hook and line is primordial, an inherited characteristic dating back in human evolution to the days of bushy-browed Neanderthal Man.

Long before the wheel, fire, or tools and weapons were discovered by ancient man, he had discovered how to catch fish to eat. This fact has been authenticated dozens of times by the discovery of ancient drawings on the walls of caves inhabited by those earliest cousins of ours. Artifacts of American Indian tribes inhabiting inland areas of North America depict annual treks to the oceans of the continent for the express purpose of catching a year's supply of seafood, most of which was fish.

The tendency to take and eat fish persisted down through time as humanity developed toward what we dare call "civilized man" as he exists today.

Science has concluded that the urge to catch fish must be catalogued as "primal," since it has been a consistent part of the known history of mankind through the ages. Little wonder that modern man, with his leisure-blessed life, answers the urge to fish even though the basic need no longer exists.

Though little is known of the methods ancients used to catch their fish, fishing today has been so thoroughly explored and developed that it approaches the category of a science. Where ancient man spent huge numbers of hours taking fish by his crude methods, modern man spends huge numbers of dollars in what essentially is the same pursuit. The tab picked up by American sport fishermen each year in this country exceeds $5 billion, which is getting up into the bracket of the nation's heat, light, and power bills, or its total telephone bills.

Sport or science?

As astonishing as $5 billion may seem to some observers, a further "staggering" statistic tells us that more participant money is spent annually in this country on fishing than is spent by fans on baseball and football combined.

Where does this information leave the average angling fan? For one point it could be considered a status symbol just to be part of a group that can somehow afford to pony up a share of $5 billion annually.

But that isn't quite a true picture, because while some fishermen lay out important amounts of dough for such an exotic sport as big-game fishing, the average guy and gal who fish for equally average game fish actually spend relatively little because there are so many fishermen to split the tab.

Many writers on the subject are inclined to eulogize fishing and fishermen. Some have gone so far as to state that they have never met a dishonest fisherman. Former President Herbert Hoover listed fishing as "the great leveler."

Unfortunately, many of us have seen and despised the seamier side of this same picture.

Just as there are game-hogs among hunters, so are there fish-hogs among anglers. Poaching out of season, taking over the allowed daily creel limit, and taking more fish than can possibly be used are all part of the modern angling scene.

In addition, since the mid-60s a new "disease" has invaded the ranks of sport fishermen. I call it "Patchitis," a word coined to express my dismay over the growing tendency among anglers to compete with each other for awards, usually shoulder patches and similar displays, for the biggest fish or the most fish or some of each, complicated by further acclaim for the angler who can achieve both in the shortest length of time.

Who needs the intense pressure generated by competitive fishing? Certainly not me. But there are persons to whom such activities are the *raison d'être* for their fishing exploits. If that is their bag, so be it. They have a right to aim their fishing "druthers" in any direction that best suits them, so long as they stay within existing laws.

In terms of both moral appreciation and practical conservation of natural resources, it galls me to see dead and wasted marlin stacked on fishing docks like cordwood. I also have seen, too many times, literally hundreds of bluefish brought ashore and left to lie in the sun while pictures were snapped showing each angler of the "lucky" party standing behind the catch as though it were a trophy scene. To me it always seemed a "traumatic scene"—one I long to change.

In all fairness to other opinions, however, that is just one man's view. That it leans more toward conservation of all fishing resources than do the views of those who follow the tournament trail is no assurance that any measurable improvement will accrue as a result of my stating it.

The main point that should be considered by all anglers on both sides of the fence is whether America's sport-fishing fraternity, as a whole, can any longer afford to view fish populations as "limitless."

I have advised all beginning anglers who have asked me to try the heat of competitive fishing before making a decision to go one way or the other in their fishing philosophy. If the utter waste of competitive angling for trophies instead of for pure pleasure doesn't clash with an individual's principles, then by all means go that route.

But I do not believe that we anglers any longer have a long-range right to waste the waning fish populations of North America and its coastal waters, though as yet no law or regulation really agrees with me.

This puts the matter squarely in the hands of the persons most concerned—the fishermen themselves.

Well, you may ask, don't the states show their concern for maintaining fish populations by regulations aimed at controlling depletion of fishing resources?

Not only fishermen are to blame

One answer to that question may be found in the bass management policies now so popular in a few states.

Maryland, for example, permits year-round fishing for largemouth and smallmouth bass. This, of course, includes the spawning season for both species. Biologists in Maryland claim that closed seasons during the spawning period do no good whatever for the basic population, but instead merely deny novice anglers the opportunity to catch bass when they are more vulnerable than they are at other times.

To this confessed layman, the idea, or theory, that taking roe-laden females before they have spawned or removing the nest-guarding males before the eggs have hatched does no harm is, to me at least, a bucket of hogwash.

That bald statement flies in the face of the opinions of accredited specialists who presumably have researched their subject. In defense of my own position it is fair to say that despite having asked numerous times for proof that spawning-period fishing is harmless, I have never seen it.

I am willing to admit that year-round fishing for bass produces more opportunity to catch fish for more novice anglers. I am also in agreement with the basic idea that, under ideal reproduction circumstances, it would be difficult, although not impossible, for hook-and-line anglers to seriously deplete most bass populations.

The catch in that theory is that few environments today can be classed as "ideal." Therefore, the excuses for "management by liberalization" simply do not hold up.

As one result of this liberalized management the biggest and best bass are continually being skimmed off the top, with the effect of decreasing the average size and numbers of fish caught by *all* anglers, both novice and expert. Add to fishing pressures the factors of water pollution that have degraded a majority of fishing waters the world over. (In this context "water pollution" should be defined as including ordinary silt, the smothering agent that takes so many fish nests annually, which in turn reduces the validity of that "ideal" factor regarding spawning success and angler harvest.)

In some lakes tested, whole year-classes of fish have been lost to silt and other pollution factors. This means that after about three or more years, when those year-classes are due to appear in the angler's creel, they simply will not be there to be caught.

When a year-class is lost, it eventually means that anglers will have available to them either the bigger and more difficult bass or little 9-inchers, which, though legal in many states, certainly are not the material of which brag-about fishing trips are made.

There is no intent here to guide the reader's thinking along lines to which I ascribe, along with thousands of other "older generation anglers." The only deliberate attempt carried by these words is to urge the beginning angler to think about the subject of his or her fishing philosophy.

I become part of a veritable army of anglers who have been around for a while and who have fished for most game fish in numerous places, when I express confusion over fisheries biologists' inconsistent management policies.

For example, while Maryland has totally liberalized fishing regulations for largemouth and smallmouth bass on the basis that a closed season does no good, it simultaneously protects striped bass during their spawning period. Incongruously, and perhaps as a result, the striper population is on the increase and the bass population is decreasing.

Where is the management logic in protecting a species whose population is virtually countless and in the same breath allowing unlimited angler harvest of a species that by estimated count amounts to a "millifraction" of 1 percent of the fish population?

These and other disturbing points will emerge for debate year after year as opposing factions contest such mixed-up management policies.

Upcoming anglers may wish to take part in future decisions concerning their sport. That is one of the reasons why I urge the reader to think and decide which of the two routes he or she wishes to follow.

Maryland is not the only state where some of the fisheries management regulations appear to be inconsistent or self-defeating.

In an objective defense of the liberalization of fisheries management policies, I have been assured by authorities that if the present policies emerge as unworkable or, for any reason, undesirable, then they will be changed soon enough to guarantee a return of most species. I find such assurances in the late afternoon of my active fishing life somewhat less than comforting. Waiting for the restoration of a dangerously depleted population of any species of fish connotes years of actionless patience, coupled with the hope that uncontrollable factors, such as pollution, will not intervene to halt progress.

The population explosion, alone, would be sufficient to cause concern in some quarters of interest in the future of American sport fishing.

There is no doubt that we have modern fishery science to thank for the present abundance and distribution of sport fishing in North America. But the trend toward scarcity cannot be denied, just as it couldn't be denied in those early days of the 20th century when biologists first began experimenting with transplanting species from native waters to similar waters all over the country.

Their objective then was to meet the growing demand for sport fishing. The impetus came from projected population growth figures. Similar projections exist today, and the scene is now complicated by the proliferation of water pollution almost every place where there is water to be polluted.

In addition to the above disturbing elements, not all fish considered as game fish by anglers are protected from commercial harvesting. Whatever regulatory action may be taken, it must assure continuance of the nation's commercial fishing industry, a vital adjunct to the nation's food supply.

Complex as the problems become in an overview of all factors, there are answers and compromises that can serve most needs. It remains only for sensible men and women to

It's up to us

299

determine which answers best suit existing and predictable circumstances as they impinge on future fish populations. To do less would be to abandon a heritage handed down from earliest man to his 20th-century counterparts: the right to catch fish and the responsibility to take only what can be used.

Granted, those ancients of the cave-days nurtured no thoughts of conserving something for tomorrow, but they at least instinctively avoided killing more than they could use.

Taking a responsible part in the future of sport fishing is the price we must pay—willingly or not—for the privilege of fishing.

Government agencies

to contact for fishing information

Alabama Dept. of Conservation and Natural Resources
64 N. Union St., Montgomery, Alabama 36104
(205) 269-7221 (Numerals in parentheses are area codes.)

Alaska Board of Fish and Game
Subport Building, Juneau, Alaska 99801
(907) 586-3392

Arizona Game and Fish Dept.
2222 W. Greenway Rd., Phoenix, Arizona 85023
(602) 942-3000

UNITED STATES

Arkansas Game and Fish Commission
Game and Fish Building, Little Rock, Arkansas 72201
(501) 371-1145

California Dept. of Fish and Game
The Resources Agency, 1416 Ninth St., Sacramento,
California 95814
(916) 445-3531

Colorado Dept. of Natural Resources, Division of Wildlife
6060 Broadway, Denver, Colorado 80216
(303) 825-1192

Connecticut Dept. of Environmental Protection
State Office Building, Hartford, Connecticut 06115
(203) 566-5460

**Delaware Dept. of Natural Resources and Environmental
Control, Division of Fish and Wildlife**
D. Street, Dover, Delaware 19901
(302) 678-4431

**Florida Dept. of Natural Resources, Game and Fish
Commission**
620 S. Meridian, Tallahassee, Florida 32304
(904) 488-2972

Georgia State Game and Fish Division
Trinity-Washington Building, 270 Washington St., S.W.,
Atlanta, Georgia 30334
(404) 656-3500

Idaho Fish and Game Dept.
600 S. Walnut, Box 25, Boise, Idaho 83707
(208) 384-3771

Illinois Dept. of Conservation
State Office Building, Springfield, Illinois 62706
(217) 525-6302

Indiana Dept. of Natural Resources, Division of Fish and Wildlife
608 State Office Building, Indianapolis, Indiana 46204
(317) 633-6344

Iowa State Conservation Commission
State Office Building, 300 Fourth St., Des Moines, Iowa 50319
(515) 281-5384

Kansas Forestry, Fish and Game Commission
Box 1028, Pratt, Kansas 67124
(316) 672-6473

Kentucky Dept. of Fish and Wildlife Resources
Capitol Plaza Tower, Frankfort, Kentucky 40601
(502) 564-3400

Louisiana Wildlife and Fisheries Commission
P.O. Box 44095, Capitol Sta., Baton Rouge, Louisiana 70804

Maine Dept. of Inland Fisheries and Game
State Office Building, Augusta, Maine 04330
(207) 289-3371

Maryland Fish and Wildlife Administration
Tawes State Office Building, Annapolis, Maryland 21401
(301) 267-5151, 5152

Massachusetts Division of Fisheries and Game
100 Cambridge St., Boston, Massachusetts 02202
(617) 727-3151

Michigan Dept. of Natural Resources
Mason Building, Lansing, Michigan 48926
(517) 373-1220

Minnesota Dept. of Natural Resources, Division of Game and Fish
301 Centennial Building, 658 Cedar St., St. Paul, Minnesota 55101
(612) 296-2894

Mississippi Game and Fish Commission
Robert E. Lee Office Building, 239 N. Lamar St.,
P.O. Box 451, Jackson, Mississippi 39205
(601) 354-7333

Missouri Dept. of Conservation
P.O. Box 180, Jefferson City, Missouri 65101
(314) 751-4115

Montana Fish and Game Dept.
Helena, Montana 59601
(406) 449-3186

Nebraska Game and Parks Commission
P.O. Box 30370, 2200 N. Thirty-third St., Lincoln, Nebraska 68503
(402) 434-0641

Nevada Dept. of Fish and Game
Box 10678, Reno, Nevada 89510
(702) 784-6214

New Hampshire Fish and Game Dept.
34 Bridge St., Concord, New Hampshire 03301
(603) 271-3421

New Jersey Dept. of Environmental Protection, Division of Fish, Game and Shellfisheries
Box 1390, Trenton, New Jersey 08625
(609) 292-2965

New Mexico Dept. of Game and Fish
State Capitol, Santa Fe, New Mexico 87501
(505) 827-2143

New York Dept. of Environmental Conservation, Fish and Wildlife Division
50 Wolf Rd., Albany, New York 12201
(518) 457-5690

North Carolina Wildlife Resources Commission
325 N. Salisbury St., Raleigh, North Carolina 27611
(919) 829-3391

North Dakota State Game and Fish Dept.
2121 Lovett Ave., Bismarck, North Dakota 58501
(701) 224-2180

Ohio Dept. of Natural Resources, Division of Wildlife
Fountain Square, Columbus, Ohio 43224
(614) 466-4603

Oklahoma Dept. of Wildlife Conservation
1801 N. Lincoln St., P.O. Box 53465, Oklahoma City,
Oklahoma 73105
(405) 521-3851

Oregon Fish Commission
307 State Office Building, Portland, Oregon 97201
(503) 229-5671

Pennsylvania Fish Commission
P.O. Box 1673, Harrisburg, Pennsylvania 17120
(717) 787-6593

Rhode Island Dept. of Natural Resources, Division of Fish and Wildlife
83 Park St., Providence, Rhode Island 02903
(401) 277-2784

South Carolina Wildlife Resources Dept.
Box 167, 1015 Main St., Columbia, South Carolina 29202
(803) 758-2561

South Dakota Dept. of Game, Fish and Parks
State Office Building, Pierre, South Dakota 57501
(605) 224-3381

Tennessee Fish and Game Commission
Box 40747, Ellington Agricultural Center, Nashville,
Tennessee 37220
(615) 741-1431

Texas Parks and Wildlife Dept.
John H. Reagan Building, Austin, Texas 78701
(512) 475-2087

**Utah State Dept. of Natural Resources, Division of Wildlife
Resources**
1596 W. North Temple, Salt Lake City, Utah 84116
(801) 328-5081

**Vermont Agency of Environmental Conservation, Fish
and Game Dept.**
Montpelier, Vermont 05602
(802) 828-3371

Virginia Commission of Game and Inland Fisheries
4010 W. Broad St., Box 11104, Richmond, Virginia 23230
(804) 770-4974

Washington Dept. of Fisheries
115 General Administration Building, Olympia, Washington
98504
(206) 753-6623

West Virginia Dept. of Natural Resources
1800 Washington St. E., Charleston, West Virginia 25305
(304) 348-2754

**Wisconsin Dept. of Natural Resources, Division of Forestry,
Wildlife and Recreation**
Box 450, Madison, Wisconsin 53701
(608) 266-2243

Wyoming Game and Fish Dept.
Box 1589, Cheyenne, Wyoming 82001
(307) 777-7631

Alberta Dept. of Lands and Forests
Natural Resources Building, Edmonton T5K 2E1
(403) 229-4461

**British Columbia Dept. of Recreation and Conservation,
Fish and Wildlife Branch**
Parliament Buildings, Victoria
(604) 387-6409

**Manitoba Dept. of Mines, Resources and Environmental
Management**
Winnipeg R3C 0V8
(204) 946-7120

**New Brunswick Dept. of Natural Resources, Fish and Wildlife
Branch**
Centennial Building, Fredericton
(506) 453-2433

Newfoundland Dept. of Tourism, Wildlife Division
Confederation Building, St. John's
(709) 722-0711, ext. 327

Nova Scotia Dept. of Lands and Forests, Wildlife Division
Box 516, Kentville
(902) 678-4198

**Ontario Ministry of Natural Resources, Division of Fish
and Wildlife**
Whitney Block, 99 Wellesley St. W., Toronto M7A 1W3
(416) 965-4704

CANADA

Prince Edward Island Dept. of Environment and Tourism, Fish and Wildlife Division
P.O. Box 2000, Charlottetown
892-3561, ext. 34

Quebec Dept. of Tourism, Fish and Game
Parliament Buildings, Complex "G," Quebec City
(418) 643-8452

Saskatchewan Dept. of Natural Resources
Government Administration Building, Regina S4S 0B1
(306) 522-1691

Yukon: Environment Canada, Fisheries Service
1100A 1st. Ave., Whitehorse, Yukon Territory
(403) 667-2235

Glossary

As is true of most sports, fishing has its own language. Many times the words, terms, and expressions of this language are used with little regard for grammatical accuracy or hairline definitions. Some have gradually come to be spelled phonetically, as an aid to pronunciation.

But whatever the reason that deviations from accepted practices occur, if the end result is good communications among anglers, then the objective has been met.

It is, therefore, with no apologies to my old English professor that the following elements of "fishing lingo" are offered for the enlightenment of all anglers, especially beginners, to help them understand what the oldtimers are talking about.

Action

As used by fishermen, the word usually refers to the stiffness or limberness of a fishing rod—as in medium action, light action, heavy action, dry-fly action, wet-fly action, streamer action. A secondary but often used definition refers to the movement of a fishing lure as it is reeled through the water.

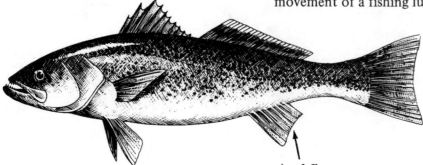

Anal fin

The fin located on the bottom of the fish's body closest to its tail.

Angleworm

Any earthworm used for bait.

Aquatic organisms

Usually defined as the whole range of plant and animal life that exists in healthy bodies of fresh water.

Artificial reef

Relatively recent innovations, artificial reefs are manmade structures or obstructions placed on the sea bottom to attract game fish.

Theoretically, they attract small crustaceans that attract baitfish that, in turn, attract game fish.

The idea arose from the experiences of anglers who fished over or around sunken ships, barges, and other objects.

In later years there has been a lot of scientific research on the best materials to use for creating reefs. Among useful materials: old auto tires, concrete blocks and other large riprap, huge piles of oystershells or clamshells, etc.

Backlash

As used by anglers, a "bird's nest" of tangled line resulting from improper control of conventional reel spools during the

310

cast. With insufficient thumb pressure on the reel spool during a cast, the spool revolves faster than the line flows out. Coils of loosened line become tangled together and the whole tangle reels backwards onto the spool. With bad backlashes, it is frequently cheaper to cut the line and replace it rather than to waste good fishing time trying to untangle it.

On fixed-spool (spinning) reels, a similar condition is called a "fluff" and occurs most often when too much line is on the spool. Under such conditions a fluff of tangled monofilament line may come off the spool as a mass of loops and will jam tight as it hits the rod guides. Another cause of "fluffs" is twisting of the line, such as might occur with some spinner-type lures.

Baitfish
Spelled as one word instead of two, an all-inclusive word used to describe all species of food or forage fish preyed upon by game fish. In many parts of North America's coastal waters the word is shortened to *bait*. *Baitfish* (or *bait*) is used generally when the speaker doesn't really know which species of baitfish he's talking about.

Barbless hooks
Hooks that have had the barbs pinched shut, or are made without barbs. They are used by some anglers for all sport fishing because they require an extra degree of skill to land fish thus hooked. In many catch-and-return trout streams the use of barbless hooks is required by law.

The growing fraternity of anglers who want the thrill of fishing with minimum harm to fish often pinch the barbs of their hooks shut with pliers.

Many plug-casting anglers prefer to use barbless hooks, even on plugs equipped with the normal treble-hooks, because they make the unhooking chore much easier and help avoid personal injury when the angler is fishing for any of the well-toothed species.

Beam
The width of a boat at its widest point along the gunwale.

Billfish
A plural word that encompasses all species of marlin and sailfish plus swordfish. In other words, all fish having "bills," or spearlike noses, are lumped into the category called billfish.

Bird's nest
See **Backlash**.

Bloodworms
One of the most widely used live baits for taking saltwater or brackish-water fish. Bloodworms are marine organisms; that is, they are found only in saltwater environments, usually saltwater marshes, and are gathered by wholesale bait dealers for distribution to tackle and bait stores.

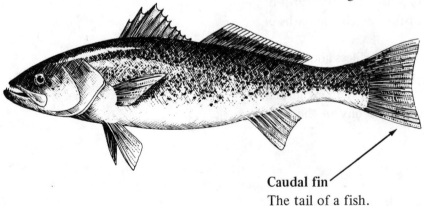

Bobber
A float made of cork, wood, or plastic attached to a fishing line at a distance from the hook that depends on water depth. When a fish takes the bait, the bobber jerks or *bobs* under the water signaling a bite.

Bow
Pronounced "bough," the front of a boat.

Bunker
A regional name for menhaden.

Butterfish
A species of oceanic forage or food fish used mainly for bluefish chumming but often used for surf fishing as well.

Caudal fin
The tail of a fish.

Chine
The junction of the sides and bottom of a boat.

Chum slick
The skim of oil on the water surface that rises from ground menhaden or other baitfish used for chumming. The combined scent and taste draws fish to the ground bait.

Conventional reel
A reel on which the spool revolves as compared to the fixed spool of a spinning reel.

Crayfish
Freshwater crustaceans that look like miniature lobsters, claws and all. Often called crawdads or crawfish. Crayfish are prime bait for most freshwater game fish, especially after they have just sloughed their shells and before the new shells harden.

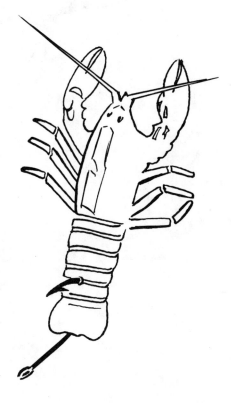

Crayfish or crawdads usually hide under rocks in freshwater streams. Fishermen often work in pairs to catch crayfish for bait. One man will turn over rocks where the crayfish hide, while his companion stands in the water several yards downstream with a small net spread.

Crayfish can be trapped with a fine mesh net weighted to lay flat on the bottom and baited with any kind of food that will stay on the net against the pull of the current. This method works best when the net is set in an eddy current or in a dead spot behind any large obstruction. With a string tied to each corner, the net can be quickly lifted out of the water to trap crayfish feeding on the bait.

Cutting board
Any piece of wood that can be laid on the sand so that bait can be cut on a solid surface instead of on soft sand. Often called a bait-board. Experienced surf fishermen carry bait-boards at all times, if only to prevent dulling the edges of bait knives in the sand.

Dew worm
See **Night crawler**.

Dorsal fin
The large fin that runs lengthwise along the fish's back, sometimes divided into two parts, a spiny part and a soft part.

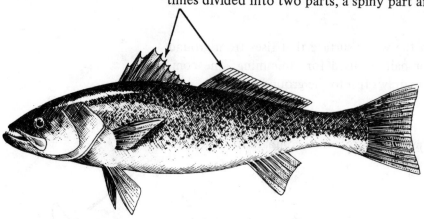

Doughballs
Bait for carp and suckers. Aside from the usual flour-and-water mixture used to make the dough, the rest of the ingredients have as many variations as there are carp and sucker fishermen.

Most doughball experts use various scents: fish oils, bits of canned tuna fish, oil from a can of sardines, anise oil, and a host of others. One senior-citizen carp fisherman I know always mixes his doughballs with hundred-proof bourbon.

Dry-fly dressing
A specially made liquid, usually with a paraffin base. The dressing applied to a dry fly makes it float properly. A must for dry-fly fishing.

Dummy line
A trolling rig used by some charter captains to help put fish in the boat, usually made of stout cord, long leaders, and heavy weights of up to a pound or more. Lures used for dummy lines are the same as those used on the trolling rods being fished astern. Among some fishermen, dummy lines are looked upon with disfavor.

Ebb tide
Tide flowing outward, toward the ocean.

Felts

Pads of dense felt cemented or clamped on wading boots or wading shoes to provide firm footing when wading among slippery rocks of trout streams. Felts have saved many an angler from injury.

Ferrule

Pronounced "fair-rule"; the metal male and female fittings where fishing rod sections are joined.

Ferrule cement

Special heat-sensitive glue used to firmly attach male and female ferrules to rod sections.

Fish finder

1. Fathometers (depth finders), which have been used on boats and ships for many years as part of the navigational equipment, used by boat owners to locate schools of fish. Fathometers produce one signal indicating bottom depth and intermediate signals for schools of fish that are between the hull of the boat and the sea (lake, river) bottom. Many charter and private skippers cruise until they see a school of fish on the fathometer before they drop anchor or put trolling baits overboard.

2. A specific type of terminal tackle (fishing rig) used mainly by surf fishermen. A drawing of a fish-finder rig is shown on page 171.

Fishing vest

One of the freshwater angler's most useful pieces of equipment.

Made oversize to remain roomy, even with all the numerous pockets filled with flies and other gear, fishing vests today usually come equipped with lined, waterproof pockets to hold either fish or lunches and coffee bottles.

Float fishing

A method of angling from a boat that is floating (or drifting) with the current instead of being anchored. The method often is called "drift fishing."

Floater fishing

A variation of bobber or cork float fishing from an anchored boat. (See **Bobber.**)

Flood tide

Tide flowing inward, away from the ocean.

Fluff

See **Backlash.**

Fly leader (fly-fishing leaders)

Distinguished from all other leaders in that they are tapered from large (where the leader joins the fly line) to small (at the fly or tippet end).

Many fly fishermen prefer to make their own tapered leaders to suit the type flies they are using, the fishing circumstances, and the action of the fly rod. Hand-tied tapered fly leaders are made, usually, by tying 18-inch lengths of monofilament leader material together using the blood-knot. (See page 263.) Beginning at the fly line, each 18-inch length of leader material is smaller in diameter than the one preceding it, thus providing adequate leader rigidity (when tied correctly) to carry the fly through the air, imparting the energy of the fly line to a finished cast.

Fly-line dressing

This term dates back to the days when fly lines were made of ingeniously braided silk, which, when properly dressed, would float for long periods before needing redressing.

With today's modern fly lines, the word "dressing" does not actually apply any more. Modern fly lines have waterproof plastic coatings and need no "dressing" to keep them dry. But such lines do need cleaning to get rid of accumulated scum.

Most fly lines sold today come with a can of line dressing, also called line cleaner.

Freeboard

The amount of boat that protrudes above the surface of the water. Safe load limits are determined in part by the freeboard remaining after a certain load is in the boat and evenly distributed. The smaller the freeboard dimension—from gunwale to water surface—the greater the hazard.

Fry
Recently hatched or very small adult fish. A school of "fry": a group of young fish that have hatched recently and are on their own.

Gaff
A single-hooked instrument with a sturdy handle, used to land fish too large for a net. Most fish are gaffed by slipping the sharpened hook point under one gill, but some fish require sterner—and fatal—methods, such as hooking through the body. Fish which you may want to release should be hooked only through one jaw.

Gang hooks
Three hooks with one common shank and hook eye, more often called "treble hooks" by sport fishermen. Treble or gang hooks are used on a variety of artificial lures, such as the plugs used for bass, pickerel, and many saltwater species.

Grass shrimp
A small shrimp found in well-grassed tidal water shallows, hence the name. Grass shrimp are prime bait for chumming striped bass and perch. They are usually harvested with roller-type shrimp nets pushed by hand and are kept alive in live-boxes until used.

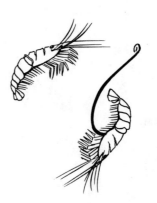

Gunwale
Pronounced and sometimes spelled gunnel, the top edge of a boat's hull.

Hard crab
A stage in the life cycle of the crab, which occurs when the shell hardens, after the soft crab stage.

Hellgrammite
The larval stage of the dobsonfly, found in most freshwater streams. Has an elongated dark brown or black body with numerous legs and leglike appendages and strong jaws that

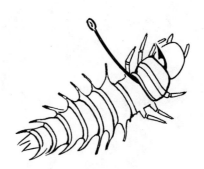

resemble pincers. It is one of the most effective of all live baits for smallmouth bass.

Keel

The longitudinal timber or plate of a boat running from stern to bow along the centerline of, and often projecting from, the bottom of the boat.

Keelson

Often pronounced "kelson," the inside backbone of a boat running from stern to bow along the centerline and usually attached to the top of the keel through the hull.

Knot strength

That portion of the tested line strength remaining after a knot has been tied in the line. Special knots, many of which are shown elsewhere in this book, retain up to 100 percent of line strength. Other knots, not recommended for fishing, reduce line strength by as much as 50 percent or more.

Larvae

An early stage in the life of an insect. An insect egg hatches to produce the larva of that insect. After passing through the larval stage, which may include several molts and even a complete change of form, the insect reaches the final adult form.

Line twist

Twists in the line usually caused by lures that spin in the water. In the case of braided lines even minor line twist becomes readily noticeable. With the advent of monofilament fishing lines, this term has taken on added importance. Monofilament lines that are badly twisted may be deformed and lose test strength.

In the case of mono lines the twist may not become apparent until it causes a series of "birds' nests" as the line coils off the reel and tries to twist up on itself. Unbelievable tangles can result from too much line twist, especially where spinning reels are being used. The section on **twisted fishing line** (Fishing tips and techniques, p. 260) will tell you what to do to avoid such problems.

L.O.A.
Length Over All, the longest dimension of a boat from the stern to the tip of the bow, measured along the deck. Many sailboats are measured by length at the water line, which understandably would be a smaller dimension than L.O.A.

Marine organisms
The whole range of plant and animal life that exists in the oceans of the world.

Menhaden
A forage or trash fish highly prized for its oil and other by-products for fertilizer and related uses. Often ground for chum or used as cut bait in surf fishing.

Milt
The sperm of male fish.

Monofilament
Single-strand fishing line, as contrasted with braided line (mono, meaning one; filament, meaning strand). Most fishing line used for spinning is monofilament line. Fishing leaders also are monofilament.

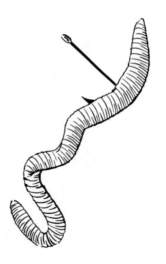

Night crawler
A large earthworm often found after dark on the surface of the ground.

Pectoral fins
Fins located on the side of the body directly behind and sometimes slightly below the gills.

Peeler crab
A crab that has begun to shed its shell. The stage immediately following the hard-crab stage.

Popping bug
The category of artificial bass lures known as "bugs." Popping bugs are distinguished from other bugs by a scooped-out front which catches the water surface and digs in, or "pops" when worked with the rod tip.

Red worm
See **Bloodworms.**

Reel seat
The piece of hardware on a fishing rod that holds the reel in place with threaded rings or similar devices.

Riffle
Usually, that part of a trout stream where the water flows over a gravel bed or rocky area, producing "riffles" on the surface. Riffles are good places to fish for trout because the broken surface provides visual cover for the fish and most trout prefer to feed in riffles.

Roe
The eggs of a female fish.

Sand fleas
A small, hump-backed crustacean found on ocean beaches. As each wave recedes, the wash will reveal sand fleas digging frantically to get back under the sand.

With little effort a supply of fleas can be caught and kept in a bucket of wet sand. They are prime bait for most inshore fish taken in the surf.

Sand spike
A rod-holder used mainly by surf fishermen. It is a piece of tubing, usually about 18 or more inches long, with a spike or spade attached on one end. By stabbing the spike into the sand the tube can be used to hold the butt and part of the handle of a surf-fishing rod while waiting for a bite, while baiting up another rod, or just to rest the angler's arms. Sand spikes will not hold against the strike and pull of a big fish. The main purpose is to eliminate laying the rod and reel down in the sand.

Sea clams
A large species of saltwater clam usually referred to as bait clams but also valued for making clam chowder and other clam dishes. Widely used as bait for ocean-bottom fishing and for surf fishing in some areas.

Sea worms

A marine, or saltwater, organism widely used for live bait by saltwater anglers. Sea worms are more popular in the New England region than elsewhere.

Slack tide

A period of no current between tide changes. There is a slack tide at the end of the ebb tide and another at the end of the flood tide.

Slick

1. As used by trout fishermen, the opposite of a riffle, usually denoting deeper, slower-moving water and good for big trout.

2. The oily scum produced by chumming for saltwater fish: "chum-slick."

Slough

1. Pronounced "slew," a depression or ditch in the sea bottom usually parallel to a beach. Sloughs are important to anglers fishing the surf because it is there most game fish are found.

Experienced surf men can read incoming waves and tell where a slough is located by the way waves crest before reaching the beach.

2. Pronounced "sluff," the act of shedding an old skin or shell: a crab sloughs off its old shell.

Smelt

A species of forage or baitfish, highly prized by saltwater fishermen.

Soft clams (manoes, mananoes):

Thin-shelled members of the clam family that have long syphons protruding from one end of the shells. The so-called Ipswich, or New England, clam is a soft clam highly prized as a table delicacy and when used as chum and bait for striped-bass fishing in areas where the soft clam is abundant.

Soft crab

For at least one tide after a crab sheds its shell, the new shell will be soft and pliable, often described as "tender as a baby's eye." Soft crabs make excellent bait for all game fish using inshore waters. Striped bass, especially, are fond of roaming the shallows where crabs move in with the tides to shed.

Solunar tables

Tables based upon phases of the moon and other factors said to affect the lives and movements of all animal life, especially fish. Used to predict peak periods of activity.

The Solunar Tables were originated by the late John Alden Knight. They have been around longer than I have and are still being published in daily newspapers and other media in certain areas.

Like the nationally famed Hagerstown Almanac, John Alden Knight's theory holds water much of the time.

Spinning reel

A reel with a fixed spool; line flows off over the rim or edge of the spool. Contrary to its name, a spinning reel does not spin.

Stern

The back or rear of a boat.

Structure fishing

A term of recent origin used by freshwater bass fishermen to describe a particular method of finding lurking bass in relatively deep water. A "structure" in that context would be any underwater obstruction, such as a sunken tree, a pile of stone, a sharp rise or a sharp dropoff in bottom contour. All such places are considered prime bass hideouts. Today's professional bass fishermen often use fathometers (depth finders) to locate such changes in bottom contour before casting their plugs or baits.

Swivels

A revolving link between fishline and terminal tackle, used between line and leader whenever a lure or bait has a tendency to spin or twist in the water. The swivel lets the lure or bait spin without twisting the fishing line.

Teaser

An artificial lure without any hooks, used mainly for big-game fishing for such species as marlin, sailfish, and sword-fish. Teasers are usually trolled from the center of the boat transom about 10 or 15 feet astern and are supposed to do just what the name implies—tease lurking marlin into looking over the real baits being trolled farther astern.

Terrestrial insects

The opposite of aquatic insects. As used by trout fishermen the word usually denotes extremely small land-based insects that live near streams, and upon which trout feed when the insects fall into the water.

Thermocline

Used mainly with reference to lakes, the point in water depth at which the temperature and oxygen levels change markedly. In general, little game-fish life can be expected below the thermocline because there usually is insufficient oxygen at those depths to support life for any prolonged period.

Thermoclines are formed (in lakes deep enough for the phenomenon to occur) by very cold water, for example, from springs, flowing into the lake. Since cold water is "heavier" than warm water, it settles to the bottom beneath the sun-warmed upper layers. The line of demarcation usually is a sharp one in lakes not disturbed by high winds and accompanying waves, which would tend to mix the two layers.

Transom

The timbers or other material across the stern of a boat that close off the back.

Tippet

The last, or smallest-diameter section of a tapered fly leader. Can be replaced as tippet length is used up by tying on different flies. Normal tippet length is about 18 inches and should be replaced when it has shortened to about 12 inches.

Treble hooks
See **Gang hooks.**

Ventral fin

Fins located on the bottom of the body ahead of the anal opening and closest to the body cavity in which the reproductive organs are located.

Wading staff

A necessity when wading trout streams with heavy currents flowing across slippery areas. A staff may be as simple as a sapling cut off to suitable length, or it may be a manufactured model.

"Working"

Many lakes and almost all ponds are said to be "working," much as a vat of mashed grapes works (bubbles) in the wine-making process. Usually, vegetable matter growing on the bottom dies off and begins to decay. Bubbles of organic gases rise to the surface, along with unsightly gobs of decaying plants and algae.

All good ponds and most shallow lakes benefit from working annually. Once the natural interchange ends, the water will become clear and fishable again and the oxygen content will increase.

Though some northern waters never get warm enough to work, most lakes and ponds go through the cycle.

Index

Smelt, 321
Smith Island, 170
Smith Mountain Lake, Va., 114, 120, 138, 140, 148
  accommodations, 285
  best fishing time, 286
  development of fishing, 15
  shoreline, 286
  species available, 285
  tackle, 32, 34
Snags, device to free lures from, 274-275
Solunar tables, 322
South Carolina coast, *see* Carolina coast
Spawning
  period, fishing during, 61, 297, 298
  run, shad, 88, 89-92
  run, yellow perch, 131-132
Spinner-baits, how to use, 44, 50, 52
Spinner/fly combinations, 82-83
Spinner-minnow rig for pickerel and northern pike, 97
Spinners
  for chain pickerel, 102
  for smallmouth bass, 61
  underwater, working, 47-48
Spinning lures for panfish, 127
Spinning tackle
  for bonefish, 230
  for channel bass, 162, 164
  for cobia, 182
  for flounder, 175
  for largemouth bass, 34, 36
  reel, 220, 322
  for shad, 92
  for smallmouth bass, 61
  for striped bass, 148
  for trout fishing, 82-84
  for walleyes, 115
  for weakfish, 198
Spool reel, 34
Spoons
  for chain pickerel, 102
  for striped bass trolling, 142
  weedless, 39, 47
Sport fishing
  basic principles, 18-19
  defined, 16
  money spent on, 7
  popularity of, 8-9
  time spent, 9
Squid, 149, 175, 197

Staff, wading, 324
Stern, 322
Still fishing, 97, 126
Stocking, necessity of, 68, 71
Storage on board boat, 268-269, 274
Streamer flies
  for bonefish, 230
  fished with light spinning tackle, 83
  how to use, 81-82
  knot for attaching, 263
  trolling rig for trout, 85
  typical patterns, 82
  for yellow perch, 132
Strike signals, 80
Stringer, 176
  correct use, 267
  varieties, 266
Striped bass, 15, 32
  adaptation to fresh water, 138, 140
  artificial lures, 152, 154-155
  average weight and length by age, 156
  in Chesapeake Bay, 136, 286-287, 289
  chumming, 143-144, 146, 147
  drift-fishing, 146-148
  feeding habits, 140
  as food fish, 136
  migration, 136
  range, 137
  Santee-Cooper Reservoir, S.C., 284
  schooling tendencies, 140, 156
  sport fishing season, 136
  surf fishing, 148-149, 152
  transplant programs, 14, 137-138
  trolling, 142-143
  world record, 135
Structure fishing, 37, 322
Styrofoam cooler as baitkeeper, 270
Suckers, doughball bait for, 314
"Sulk periods," muskie, 109
Summer flounder
  as food fish, 172, 178
  range, 174
  world record, 173
Sunfish, *see* Bluegill, Crappies, Pumpkinseed
Surf, reading, 215
Surf fishing
  for bluefish, 214
  care of tackle, 257
  essential equipment, 164, 166
  fish-finder rig, 171, 315
  fishing sloughs, 275